ONCE ROUND THE SUN

The Story of the International Geophysical Year

THE MACMILLAN COMPANY
NEW YORK · CHICAGO
DALLAS · ATLANTA · SAN FRANCISCO
LONDON · MANILA

BRETT-MACMILLAN LTD.
TORONTO

The International Geophysical Year
is timed to coincide with a period of
maximum activity on the sun; and
here is surely one of the finest photographs of a sunspot ever taken.

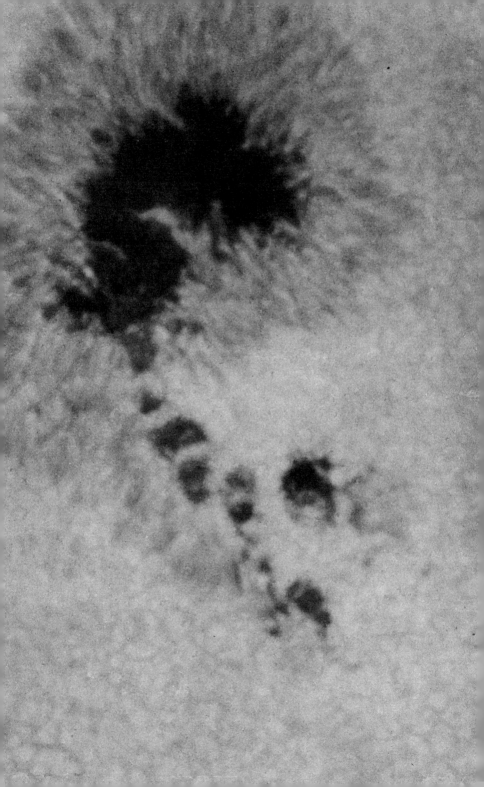

ONCE ROUND THE SUN

The Story of the
International Geophysical Year

RONALD FRASER

THE MACMILLAN COMPANY, NEW YORK
1958

© 1957 by Ronald Fraser

PRINTED IN THE UNITED STATES OF AMERICA
THIRD PRINTING, 1958

C and H.
2.77
8-19-58 ag
9-16-58 cdm

Library of Congress Catalog Card Number: 58-6229

TO
THE NEXT GENERATION

CONTENTS

Page

INTRODUCTION: The Age of Scientific Exploration   xiii

PART I

ON THE BOUNDARIES OF THE KNOWN WORLD

Chapter

1. THE SPINNING EARTH 19

    Sizes and shapes. The spinning earth. The twenty-
    four-hour day. The day is seasonal. Now and then.
    The earth's main magnetic field. The precession of
    the earth's axis of rotation. Magnetic flip-flops.
    The wandering Poles. Glaciers. Continental drift.
    Still another school.

2. CLIMATE AND WEATHER 34

    Greenhouse without glass. Water vapour. Cloud
    patterns. Glaciers again. Carbon dioxide. Man-
    made climate. Water vapour and the winds of heaven.
    The age of sail. The age of air travel. The jet streams.
    The problem of global circulation in the atmosphere.
    Fuelling the atmospheric heat engine. Repaying a
    debt to the earth. Poleward of 30° north and south.
    The circumpolar vortex. Cut-offs north and south.
    Families of cyclones. Cause or effect? The next phase.

3. CURRENTS, WAVES AND TIDES 51

    Ocean gyres. Deep-sea currents. The anatomy of the
    Atlantic. Long waves. Ocean tides. Changes in sea-
    level.

4. PATTERNS IN THE OUTER ATMOSPHERE . . . 60

    A study in solar control. The chemistry of the outer
    atmosphere: oxygen; ozone; sodium; fragments of
    water vapour; nitrogen. The night airglow. Ions
    electrons and radio. Layers in the ionosphere: night
    and day; solar tides and the compass needle; the
    F_2 layer and the winds of summer; sporadic E.
    "Whistlers". The ionosphere and the sun cycle.
    The aurora polaris.

Chapter   *Page*

5. SUNSPOTS AND SOLAR FLARES 79

The birth of a sunspot. The sunspot cycle. Magnetic fields of sunspots. Magnetic polarity of sunspots. The sun's magnetism. Prominences. The prominence cycle. Flares. Terrestrial effects of solar flares; instantaneous effects: magnetic crochets; radio fade-outs; atmospherics. Delayed effects: corpuscles from the sun; the genesis of a magnetic storm; characteristics of magnetic storms; displays of the aurora. Small magnetic storms.

PART II
TOWARDS NEW HORIZONS

6. A YEAR OF PLANNED OBSERVATION . . . 97

First steps. The protagonists. Ways and means. ICSU. The march of events. Co-ordination. A twenty-four hour watch on the sun. World alerts: RWD's and WMI's. World panorama.

7. ANTARCTICA 109

Facts. Antarctic telescope. Scientific exploration. Antarctic meteorology. Radio cut-offs. White-outs. Hydrogen. The earth's magnetic field. Aurorae. The ionosphere above Antarctica. Twinkling stars. Glaciers yet again. Roll-call: Norway; Japan; Australia; U.S.S.R.; France; New Zealand; United States; United Kingdom; The Commonwealth Expedition.

8. DIVISION OF LABOUR 129

Three degrees of urgency: Meteorology; Oceanography; Glaciology. Ionospheric Physics: The aurora; Geomagnetism; Cosmic rays. Seismology and Gravity. Latitudes and Longitudes.

9. ROCKETS AND SATELLITES 144

Swords and ploughshares. The IGY rocket programme. Vertical cross-section. Solar radiation. High-level winds: grenades and sodium bombs. Dynamo currents. Particle studies. Long-playing rocket. Three-stage launch. Chosen orbit. Moon's-eye view. Acquisition. The figure of the earth. Death spiral.

10. THE SUMMING UP 159

LIST OF ILLUSTRATIONS

Maximum Activity on the Sun ! . . . . *frontis.*

Facing page

The Birth of a Sunspot [1] 84

A Sunspot Pair [1] 84

The Greenwich Butterfly Diagram [1] 85

Sunspots on the Sun's Disc [1] 85

A Giant Prominence on the Sun [1] 92

Flares on the Sun [2] 92

Sydney Chapman [3] 93

Lloyd Berkner [4] 93

Mountains in Antarctica [5] 108

Mount Erebus on Ross Island [5] 109

Ice Age in Antarctica [5] 109

Glacier on the Slopes of Mount Markham [5] . . . 112

The Russian Ships *Ob* and *Lena* [6] 113

The U.S.S.R. Base at Mirny [6] 113

The United States 'Operation Deep Freeze' [7] . . 128

U.S. Air Base on McMurdo Sound [7] 128

The M.S. *Tottan* [12] 129

The Royal Society Base at Halley Bay [12] . . . 129

Recovery of Meteorological Instruments from a Skyhook
Balloon [8] 132

Decca Wind-finding Radar Apparatus [9] . . . 132

Auroral Displays in Alaska [10] 133

The Gartlein All-Sky Camera [10] 140

A Sky Camera Photograph [10] 140

ix

Facing page

The Markowitz Moon Camera [11]   141

The Moon photographed against the Stars [11]   .   .   . 141

Launching an Aerobee Rocket [7]   148

The Earth from a height of 100 miles [7]   .   .   . 149

Construction Work at Fort Churchill [7]   .   .   . 156

Rocket Records of the Sun's Spectrum [7]   .   .   . 156

The U.S. Artificial Satellite [7]   157

The Satellite's Radio Transmitter [7]   157

The illustrations listed above are due to the following:

1. Royal Greenwich Observatory
2. Professor L. d'Azambuja, Observatoire de Meudon
3. The Royal Society of London
4. Blackstone Studios
5. National Geographic Magazine
6. The Moscow Academy of Sciences
7. United States Navy
8. United States Information Service
9. Decca Manufacturing Company
10. Geophysical Institute, University of Alaska
11. U.S. Naval Observatory, Washington
12. Central Press Photos

Acknowledgements

THE photographs, with one exception, have already been acknowledged in their proper place. The exception is the Frontispiece, which I received as a Christmas card from Dr. J. Rösch, Director of the Observatoire du Pic du Midi in the Hautes Pyrénées, with the inscription "*This* is a good one!"

The line drawings have all been made specially for this book. They spring from a variety of sources—sketch blocks, letters, scientific papers, books. A fair number owe something of their style of presentation to the "Scientific American", a magazine inaccessible alas to too many: such are those on pages 38, 40, 72, 75, 77, 90.

Individual acknowledgement is due to the Scripps Institution of Oceanography for the map of the IGY island stations on page 132, and for the diagram of the Van Dorn long wave recorder on page 133.

The execution of the line drawings has been carried out by Mr. D. E. Strachan and by Mr. A. Spark. Mr. Spark, moreover, has been responsible to the publishers for their general uniformity. I thank them both.

Finally I have to thank the many colleagues who have read this or that part of the first drafts of my manuscript. The merit of the final text is due in no small measure to their expert criticism— laudatory, encouraging, dubious, and downright devastating alike. . . . The faults are mine.

The Author

INTRODUCTION

THE AGE OF SCIENTIFIC EXPLORATION

THE geographical exploration of the earth is all but finished. The days when a man set sail from a Mediterranean port to discover new lands in the west are long since past; the charting of the oceans, one of the preoccupations of the eighteenth century, is practically a closed chapter; the nineteenth-century exploration of the unknown continents has given us maps of all the great land-masses except Antarctica; few mountain peaks remain to be climbed.

The aftermath of the era of geographical exploration is, of course, very evident today. We have ocean voyages on drifting rafts; we have lone crossings of the seven seas in a bewildering variety of unsuitable vessels; we have transcontinental journeys in jeeps, jalopies, and land rovers; we have abundant write-ups of camel rides in the desert, canoeing upstream along tropical rivers, safaris in darkest Africa. But these are stories of human endeavour, not of genuine exploration, geographical or scientific.

The age of the scientific exploration of the earth is now upon us, which may indeed involve a degree of geographical exploration, but of which geography is not the essence. Its essential feature is the urge to a better understanding of the physical properties of the earth as a whole: its core, its crust, its oceans, and its atmosphere, rather than its surface topography.

Edmund Halley

Oddly enough, one of the greatest pioneers of the scientific exploration of the earth—in a word, of *Geophysics*—was a contemporary of Isaac Newton—the same Newton who laid the foundations of the physical sciences as a whole in his monumental work *Principia Mathematica*. . . . His name was Edmund Halley.

Halley is known to almost everyone, and quite rightly, as the discoverer of Halley's Comet; there is a charming picture, by an unknown French artist, of Halley being summoned from his grave in 1758—sixteen years after his death—to view the predicted return of his star. But comparatively few know of his very remarkable contributions, long before his time, to the scientific exploration of the earth.

In November 1676, while still a twenty-year-old undergraduate at Oxford, he cadged a voyage to St. Helena, from no less a person than Charles II, to make a catalogue of the southern stars. That was the origin of two epoch-making voyages, one in 1698, the second in 1699, both with the explicit aim of delineating the magnetic field of the earth at different points on the earth's surface.

From these two voyages he came back with maps of the earth's magnetic field which allowed him to speculate that the rate of rotation of the earth's core relative to its outer shell was around 0·5° per year. With proper scientific caution, he writes that 'the nice Determination of this, and several other Particulars in the Magnetic System, is reserv'd for remote Posterity'. Today, 250 years later, the relative rate of rotation of the earth's core and mantle is estimated to lie between 0·2° and 0·3° per year!

On March 6, 1716, there was observed throughout Europe a remarkable display of the aurora borealis. It was the first display of the aurora that Halley, then aged about 60, had ever seen. With characteristic impetuosity, he wrote in the same year a contribution to the *Philosophical Transactions of the Royal Society of London*, entitled *An Account of the late surprising Appearance of the Lights in the Air, on the sixth of March last, with an Attempt to explain the Principal* Phaenomena *thereof*. In this learned paper he concludes that the aurora is no "prodigy", but is caused by "magnetical effluvia" from the earth's interior, which are constrained to move along the lines of force of the earth's magnetic field. Except that we now think that the "magnetic effluvia" come from the sun, rather than from the earth's core, this guess of Halley's is once again surprisingly close to the direction of informed modern thinking. . . .

It is a curious accident of time that the tercentenary of

Halley's birth should fall in 1956, on the eve of the world's greatest effort to date to reach a new platform from which to review the present status of man's knowledge of his own planet; for on July 1 1957 begins the International Geophysical Year—a cooperative venture on the part of fifty-four nations to reach a better understanding of our environment.

IGT 1957–58

The story of the International Geophysical Year is the central theme of this book. *Once round the sun:* that is a year of time— although strictly speaking we shall have gone one and a half times round the sun between July 1, 1957, and the end of the international effort at the close of 1958! During this very interval of time the sun is passing through one of its recurrent states of enhanced eruptive activity, a period of maximum number of sunspots, solar prominences, and flares. This maximum activity on the sun, which occurs once every eleven years or so, was indeed the deciding factor in the choice of 1957–58 as a favourable time for an all-out world-wide attack on the current problems of Geophysics; for the men and women who are dedicated to the new science have found that the physics of our planet cannot be properly studied without reference to its sun.

The scientists of fifty-four nations who are co-operating in the mutually agreed programme of the IGY 1957–58 are working on the boundaries of their own knowledge of the physical world. So in order to understand why they are pressing on in certain preferred directions rather than in others, we must first find out how far they have got in their scientific exploration of the earth.

Part I of this book is therefore devoted to an attempt to outline the present boundaries of knowledge in geophysics: in the investigation of the interior of the earth, the oceans, the atmosphere, and the influence of the sun on terrestrial phenomena.

Part II deals with the programme of the International Geophysical Year: an account of the expeditions setting out into the dark continents of man's environment, viewed against the background of the areas he has already mapped. . . . An enterprise of which Edmund Halley would have approved.

PART ONE

ON THE BOUNDARIES OF THE KNOWN WORLD

CHAPTER I

THE SPINNING EARTH

THE earth moves round the sun in an oval track, that has an average radius of 93 million miles, at a speed of $18\frac{1}{2}$ miles a second. It is kept steady in its orbit, like any other planet or satellite, by two forces that exactly balance: the gravitational pull of the sun, and the centrifugal force due to its own speed. So that although it is always falling towards the sun, it never gets any nearer to it; neither does it rush off into space like a stone cast from a catapult.

Sizes and shapes

The earth is almost a sphere, but not quite. The distance from its centre to either Pole is 3,950 miles: the distance from

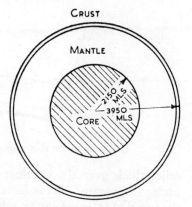

The earth's *core* is made up chiefly of molten nickel-iron. The core is held liquid under enormous internal pressures, rising to a million atmospheres at the centre, by its very high temperature. The *mantle* is a sheath of basaltic rock, surrounded by the thin *crust* we can explore from the surface.

its centre to any point on the Equator is 13 miles longer. In other words, it bulges around its middle.

The radius of the sun is 432,000 miles, that is, a hundred times that of the earth. Stated in this bald way, the real difference in size between sun and earth is perhaps not very adequately conveyed. Put more graphically, it means that the sun could contain no less than 1,300,000 bodies of the same size as the earth.

The earth is not a uniform solid sphere: it is more like a golf ball, with a liquid core, probably of molten iron, with a radius of 2,150 miles, a mantle of solid basaltic rock, and a very thin crust of the rocks the geologists know, a couple of hundred

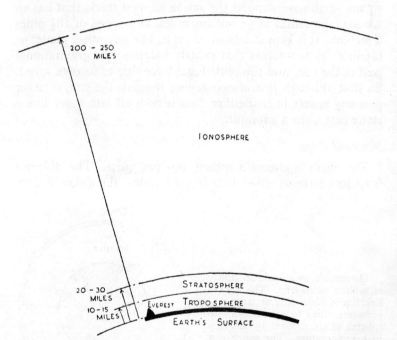

Layers in the thin skin of the earth's atmosphere.

miles thick over the continents, and only a few miles thick under the oceans. These facts come from the careful study of the speed of travel of earthquake waves at different levels below the earth's surface.

The earth's atmosphere, the canopy of air surrounding it, has no clean-cut boundary. It is thin as an onion skin, with practically no air any more at only 300 miles above the surface. It is rather arbitrarily divided into three main sheaths; the troposphere, some 10 miles thick, which is the seat of the world's weather; the comparatively calm stratosphere, 20 miles thick; and the ionosphere, the reflector of radio-waves, which is approximately 200 miles thick. The outermost region of the atmosphere is the spray-zone, where the particles of air rise and fall on the edge of space like the celluloid balls on the water-jets of a shooting gallery.

The spinning earth

The earth spins as it traverses its orbit round the sun, turning like a chicken on a spit once every 24 hours to give the procession of night and day. Moreover, the spit on which it turns is not at right angles to its direction of motion, but is tilted at an angle of $23\frac{1}{2}°$ to a line drawn perpendicular to the flat disc of its orbit: giving us the sequence of the seasons as the earth goes once round the sun in each year of $365\frac{1}{4}$ days.

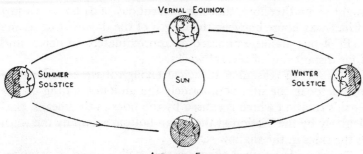

The inclination of the earth's axis of spin to the plane of its orbit gives rise to the four seasons. It is also very probably responsible for maintaining the earth's magnetic field.

Our senses don't tell us that the earth is spinning, because of course we are spinning with it. But if we aim to be participants in the age of scientific exploration, we must be constantly and acutely aware of the effects of living on a spinning earth. This might be easier if we lived at one of the Poles. Thus if we shot off a rocket horizontally from a perch at the North Pole, we should see it disappearing over the horizon, not in the direction of projection, but strongly deflected towards the right. If our perch were at the South Pole, it would sail out of sight deflected towards the left. The nearer we go to the Equator, the less obvious the effect, which vanishes on the Equator itself, where we are merely carried around with the rotating earth, standing perpendicular to the axis of spin.

But always the twist of the spinning earth is there, a maximum at the Poles, dwindling to zero at the Equator. The winds of heaven feel it, the ocean currents know it, the liquid core obeys it—this deflecting twist that the spinning earth gives to all moving things: clockwise in the northern hemisphere, against the clock in the southern hemisphere. We shall meet this deflecting force of the spinning earth—the so-called Coriolis force—many times in the sequel.

The twenty-four-hour day

At the present time, the length of the day is increasing at the rate of one or two thousandths of a second every 100 years. It might seem, therefore, that our present day of 24 hours is a sort of half-way house between the length of the day existing at the birth of our planet, estimated at approximately 10 hours, and a far-distant day of several weeks.

This sort of reasoning is logical enough if we consider only one factor in the situation, namely the undoubted drag on the earth's rotation which is caused by the tides in the oceans, particularly by the friction at the ocean bottom set up by the wash of the tides in the shallow seas.

But there is another effect on the earth's speed of rotation, which acts in just the opposite direction: and that is the effect of the *solar* tides in the earth's atmosphere, in the air above the earth's surface, rather than in the oceans, which are the main province of the moon. It is a fact that the sun, whose effect on the oceanic tides is less than half that of the moon, raises enormous tides in the earth's envelope of air, the results of which we shall meet in another connection in Chapter 4.

Why, then, has the pull of the sun such an influence on the earth's atmosphere? The answer is really very simple: the natural period of oscillation of a column of air of the height and density of our actual atmosphere is just 24 hours! In other

words, the atmosphere is in sympathetic resonance with the
period of rotation of the earth, just as in the classic examples of
the child's swing, the regiment marching in step on the sus-
pension bridge, or the goblet shattered by a particular note on

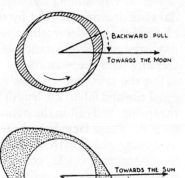

The moon, assisted by the sun,
raises tides in the oceans which re-
tard the rotation of the earth. The
sun itself raises large tides in the
atmosphere, which result in an
acceleration of the earth's rotation.

the piano. Hence the enormous daily rise and fall of the 300-
mile-deep aerial ocean as it passes under the sun, a rise and fall
quite easily observable on a sensitive barometer.

Now owing to the bounce in the atmospheric spring, high
tides in the atmosphere occur about two hours *before* mid-day,
and about two hours *before* midnight, not precisely *at* noon
and *at* midnight. This means that the sun puts an accelerating
twist on the earth in the direction of its own motion: that is,
against the retarding twist of the moon. And when you do an
accurate calculation, it turns out that the accelerating twist of
the sun and the retarding twist of the moon, acting on the earth
through the solar tides in the atmosphere, and the lunar tides
in the shallow seas, just about balance.

So it looks as if the 24-hour day were an equilibrium state:
that, true enough, the length of the day has increased from the
earliest times to the present day, but that it isn't going to go on
increasing steadily into the future. The present slow rate of increase in the length of the day may, in fact, be a temporary
trend in one direction about an equilibrium day of 24 hours,

which might well be reversed in another 100,000 years by a shrinkage of the oceans in a future glacial epoch.

The day is seasonal

We all talk among ourselves in the autumn about how the days are drawing in. But by that we only mean that the hours of daylight are decreasing: we are not asserting that the *real* day—the period of rotation of the earth—is increasing and decreasing with the seasons.

But the astronomers have found that there is a genuine seasonal rise and fall in the length of the day. The earth goes slow in the spring, and fast in the autumn, by about one thousandth of a second. These facts have been established in the last few years by timing the apparent motions of the stars with the help of hyper-accurate clocks, controlled by the natural oscillations of specially cut quartz crystals. The explanation of the facts lies chiefly in the seasonal variation in the strength of the winds, particularly the trade winds, as the sun transits to and fro across the equator: in the spring, the winds aid the eastward spin of the earth, in the autumn they hinder it.

Now and then

Quite unpredictably, the earth may suddenly go faster or slower. These sudden changes in the rate of spin of the earth, and of course in the length of the day, may occur at any time, and are superimposed on the contemporary steady increase in the length of the day, and on the regular seasonal changes. Thus for example, in 1897 the earth's rotation increased by nearly three thousandths of a second per day, while in 1914 the rotation was suddenly slowed down by a like amount.

In some ways these sporadic changes in the rate of spin are the most interesting of the lot, for they lead us to inquire more closely into the state of things in the deep interior of the earth. Jumping the argument for the moment, to arrive at the conclusion, it can be said that the cause of these sudden accelerations and decelerations in the rate of rotation of the earth is almost certainly a sudden loosening or tightening of the magnetic coupling between core and mantle.

Now for the argument... Everyone knows that the magnetic field of the earth is roughly the same as that of a gigantic bar magnet, imbedded in the earth and inclined to its axis of rotation at an angle of about 12°. But it is not generally known that the actual magnetic field can be broken down by careful analysis into two quite separate parts: the field that would be given by the big bar magnet, and another very complex magnetic field, which is the same as would be given by no less than thirteen much smaller bar magnets, lined up along thirteen different diameters of the globe.

These two magnetic fields are known as the *dipole field* and the *residual field* respectively: and for the moment our chief interest lies in the residual field. For it has been found that the residual field is drifting westward at a rate of some 12 miles per annum, which would bring it back to its present position in something like 1,600 years. This is a fantastically rapid rate of change on any geological standards; so the geomagneticians have looked for the seat of the whole phenomenon in the liquid core, where such fast changes are at least possible.

It then turns out that the residual field can be interpreted in the language of turbulent eddies in a liquid core, which is at the same time a superlative conductor of electricity—as indeed a liquid nickel–iron core would most certainly be. For such eddies, circulating near the surface of the core with a speed at the edge of the eddy of a few miles a day, would set up currents fully large enough to create the local magnetic fields actually observed.

A world map of these eddy currents, deduced from the measurements of the local magnetic fields made at the earth's surface, is quite similar in appearance to a weather chart: which in a sense it is, if our argument is correct—a weather chart of the swirls and eddies at the boundary of the liquid core. The pattern of these turbulent motions in the core must be expected to change with time, and there is evidence that it is changing. But for the moment the chief point of interest is that the whole pattern is drifting westwards, like clouds across a summer sky.

Now this can only mean that the rotation of the liquid core lags behind that of the crust and mantle; for we know that any place on the earth's surface is moving eastwards towards the rising sun. We must suppose, however, that the core is loosely hitched to the mantle by magnetic forces between the eddy currents and the electrically conducting inner surface of the mantle.

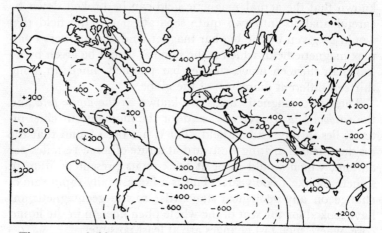

The pattern of eddy currents near the surface of the liquid core, as deduced from the local magnetic fields at the earth's surface. The whole pattern drifts westwards, against the direction of the earth's rotation. (*After Vestine.*)

Consequently, a sudden increase or decrease in the strength of the eddy currents must result in a corresponding change in the coupling of core to mantle: crust and mantle will abruptly slow down or gain in speed relative to the core. . . .

And indeed, when the history of the westward drift of the residual magnetic field over the past few decades is carefully examined, and at the same time compared with the astronomical data on the rate of the earth's rotation, there are strong hints that just at those times when the westward drift slowed down, the rotation of the crust and mantle speeded up, and vice versa! It will be exciting to see whether more extended observation and analysis will convert these hints into certainties.

The earth's main magnetic field

This fascinating discovery (or perhaps one should more appropriately say "re-discovery"!) certainly gives us the necessary confidence to inquire further into the properties of the liquid core. Can they be made to explain the earth's main magnetic field, which, as we have seen, corresponds to that of a bar magnet linked with the axis of rotation about which the whole earth spins?

Here we are on the very edge of the boundary of the known world. But the trend of speculation today is strongly in the direction of a dynamo theory of the earth's magnetic field. ...

There is a special kind of actual dynamo, well known to electrical engineers, called a *self-exciting* dynamo. This kind of

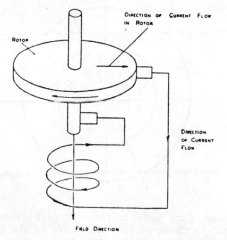

This is how an engineer's self-exciting dynamo works, delivering an electric current to its surroundings. In the earth's core, such currents are supposed to produce the earth's magnetic field.

dynamo needs only a very feeble built-in magnetic field, because the electric currents induced in the rotor are tapped off to flow in a coil around it, which enhances the magnetic field, and so maintains its motion. It is this kind of dynamo, where the material rotor is replaced by the liquid circulating in the earth's rotating core, and the material magnetic coil by lines of magnetic force "frozen" in the highly viscous molten nickel-iron of the core, which is invoked to account for the main dipole field of the earth.

The precession of the earth's axis

We may now ask ourselves: How is the circulation in the liquid core, which is necessary for the functioning of the self-exciting dynamo, maintained? The answer lies almost certainly in the bulge around the earth's Equator!

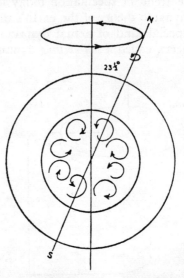

The precession of the earth's axis sets up turbulent motions in the core, which maintain the dynamo system responsible for the earth's magnetic field.

The pull of the sun (and moon) on this bulge produces a twisting force on the spinning earth which tries to tilt its axis upright, away from its natural sloping position relative to it's orbit. But the spin of the earth makes that impossible; and as a sort of dynamical compromise, the earth's axis swings, or precesses, about the vertical, once every 26,000 years. This is a very rapid motion: it means that the North Pole is moving at the rate of about 10 feet a day.

The liquid core, however, cannot follow this very fast conical motion of its containing vessel, the solid mantle. Instead, it is thrown into a complicated circulation pattern, which has been

shown to be not inconsistent with the production and maintenance of the earth's main magnetic field.

Magnetic flip-flops

This model is in harmony with the findings of the new
science of Palaeo-magnetism—the tracing of the magnetic pre-
history of the earth in the record of the rocks. Palaeo-botany and
Palaeo-zoology read the story of plant and animal pre-history
from their fossil remains. Palaeo-magnetism uses magnetic fossils, such as the grains of iron-bearing minerals frozen in the sub-
stance of once-molten lavas. When the encompassing lava was
molten, we must suppose that these magnetic granules were
permanently magnetised in the direction of the earth's mag
netic field at the time and place at which the lava was laid
down. When the lava solidified, however, the magnetised fragments of iron-ore were frozen in position. They are therefore
reliable tell-tales of the direction of the magnetic field in bygone
geological eras.

Intensive systematic study of these magnetic fossils, both in
lavas, and extensively in sedimentary rocks from very many
different parts of the world, has revealed the surprising fact
that the direction of their magnetisation is not at all necessarily
the same as it would be if they were laid down today. Sometimes they are magnetised north–south, but quite as frequently
south–north!

The most straightforward interpretation of these observations
is to suppose that the direction of the magnetic field of the earth
has reversed itself, not once but many times in the past, at irregular intervals of a few hundred thousand or a few million years.
And here the fluid-core theories of the earth's magnetic field
come once again into focus. It is inconceivable that the direction of magnetisation of a *solid* sphere could be subject to such
sudden reversals; but the motions of a fluid core might well so
change that the magnetic field of a self-exciting dynamo could
switch its direction completely. There is the further point, too,
that the reversals in the magnetisation of the rocks are total, true
flip-flops, which again is consistent with the possible behaviour
of a liquid core whose motions are subject to a spinning earth.

The wandering Poles

These sudden rapid reversals of the earth's magnetic field, which cannot have taken longer than 1,000 years or so, are not the only astonishing events which are revealed by the magnetic

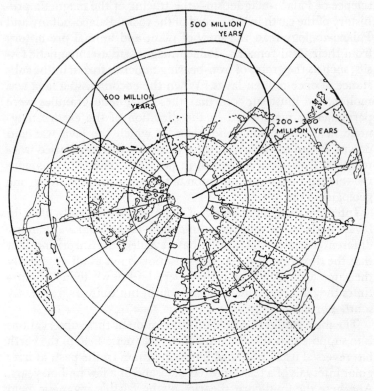

On the evidence of "magnetic fossils", the North Pole has wandered during the past 1000 million years from a point in Eastern America, over the Pacific, and up through Siberia to its present position. (*After Runcorn.*)

fossils. The direction in which the axis of the main dipole field of the earth lies has also changed markedly over the æons of geological time, quite apart from the changes in the polarity of the dipole.

If, then, we assume that the main dipole field was linked with the axis of rotation of the earth in the past, as it undoubtedly is in the present, then we are led to the sufficiently remarkable conclusion that the axis of rotation can change with time relative to the land-masses and oceans of the world: in other words, that the position of the geographic poles has wandered.

This does *not* mean that the axis of rotation of the earth, which is tilted $23\frac{1}{2}°$ against a line drawn vertically to the plane of its orbit, has changed its fixed direction in space: there are overwhelming arguments to show that the direction of the spit on which the earth turns is, aside of course from its precession, absolutely unalterable. What it does mean is that the earth, which we now recognise as a plastic sphere rather than a rigid globe, may have toppled over, now this way and now that, carrying all the continents and seas with it, so that the unalterable invisible spit on which it turns pierces the surface at different geographic positions, north and south.

Summarising now the evidence of the magnetic rocks in this matter, it is briefly this : that between 500 and 600 million years ago the North Pole lay in the Pacific Ocean; that 300 million years ago it was in Japan; and that it then wandered across the mainland of Eastern Asia to its present position in the Arctic Sea.

Glaciers

Let us pursue the argument further. . . . If the location of the Poles has altered throughout geological time, then we should find evidence of glacial action in apparently very strange parts of the world. This is of course just what we do find, and the imprint of ancient glaciers in such unlikely places as Western Australia, Central Africa, and Brazil, has led quite a number of scientists to speculate about the possibility of a toppling of the earth, that is of polar wandering, quite apart from the new evidence of the magnetic rocks.

At the present moment, however, the dating of the thick files of the geological record is not sufficiently exact to clinch the argument. What is needed is a positive assurance that the glacial deposits in Brazil occurred at the same epoch as the North Pole appears to have been situated in Japan, or that the glaciers of the African plateau coincided in time with a North Pole located in mid-Pacific.

Finally, we are at liberty to ask *why* the earth should have toppled over in the past, as indeed it appears to have done. The cause could lie deep in the interior of the earth, in the motions of the dense liquid core. But it could also be attributable to movements of the great land masses of the earth's crust: and this possibility we shall now examine more closely.

Continental drift

The idea that the continents, previously grouped in two great land masses, drifted apart some two hundred million years ago, until they occupy the positions in which we find them today, is not a new one. But direct evidence that Africa, India, and Australia once fitted like the pieces of a jigsaw puzzle around the Antarctic Continent, and subsequently drifted towards the Equator, has been heard only in the last decade.

Once again, the magnetic fossils have told their story. But this time the most important item of information is not so much the deviation of their direction of magnetisation east or west of the present magnetic axis of the earth, as their inclination to the horizontal. For a freely suspended magnet anywhere on the earth's surface aligns itself along the magnetic lines of force at that place: consequently, it hangs horizontally at the Equator, but dips—North-seeking Pole downwards in the northern hemisphere, South-seeking Pole downwards in the southern hemisphere—always more steeply as it is carried towards the Poles. From the angle of dip of the magnetic fossils, therefore, we can deduce their geographical *latitude* at the time they were laid down.

Now it has been found that the magnetic dip of Tasmanian rocks aged about 100 million years is far steeper than that of a compass needle in Tasmania today: it corresponds in fact to a position within 10° of the South Pole. The magnetic dip of rocks of about the same age from Central India gives the latitude of India 100 million years ago as 34° south of the equator. Similar measurements on South African rocks tell the same tale: 100 million years ago Africa lay far south of its present position.

Thus the evidence for the reality of continental drift, at any rate in the southern hemisphere, is accumulating rapidly. And here we should point out that the *northward* flow of the ancient glaciers in Brazil, Central Africa, India, and Western Australia fits quite naturally into this picture of the past.

Have we then to reject the idea of polar wandering as the origin of these glaciers? Not necessarily: for the concensus of opinion is that both continental drift *and* polar wandering are real phenomena, the one in fact possibly the cause of the other. Much more work has to be done in this fascinating new subject of Palaeo-magnetism before all the rapidly increasing mass of experimental data can be moulded into one self-consistent whole.

Still another school

The line of approach to the problem of the ice-ages followed in this chapter has stemmed from a consideration of the spinning earth, its liquid core, its magnetic field. But another school of thought drives in on the conundrum from quite another angle. They say that it isn't at all necessary to consider either polar wandering *or* continental drift as the mainsprings of the glacial clocks, although either or both may have been subsidiary mechanisms. They prefer a cosmical origin, looking for a reason for a general periodic cooling and heating of the entire earth, either through the accretion of meteor dust in the earth's atmosphere, which would drain it of water vapour in rainfall, or through an increase in the carbon dioxide content of the air, perhaps arising from an extra-luxuriant plant-growth, which would blanket the earth in a warmer envelope.

Properly to appreciate these speculations, however, needs a closer look at the earth's atmosphere, which deserves to be reserved for a succeeding chapter. But one thing can be said now : that whatever the origin of past ice-ages, it is not improbable that we are approaching a man-made warm period, simply because we are belching carbon dioxide into the air from our factories at a present rate of several billion tons a year!

CHAPTER 2

CLIMATE AND WEATHER

Most of us take the climate of our earth more or less for granted. We accept the fact that it is cold in winter and warm in summer, but usually we don't inquire further, to ask why the average temperature of the whole earth is what it is. When we begin to look into this question, however, we find that the balance which holds our overall climate between the two extremes of a frozen waste and a tropical swamp is extremely sensitive to quite small variations in the composition of the atmosphere, which have almost certainly occurred in the past, and may well happen in the future.

Greenhouse without glass

The earth is warmed by the radiation it catches from the sun, a tiny fraction of the total energy of the solar atomic furnace, broadcast across 93 million miles of empty space. The radiation which penetrates the atmosphere to reach the earth's surface is concentrated in quite a narrow range of wave-lengths, extending from the near infra-red, through the wave-band which our eyes register as visible sunlight, into the near ultra-violet. Oceans and continents alike absorb a part of the radiation falling on them, and are thereby heated to the point where they begin to re-radiate their trapped sunlight. But they do so like any object which is merely warm rather than white hot—not in the visible wave-band, but in the infra-red.

Now if the earth's atmosphere were entirely made up of four parts of nitrogen to one of oxygen, this infra-red radiation would pass freely out into space—and the earth would be much colder than it is, with large differences in temperature between day and night. There are, however, two minor constituents of the atmosphere which, while transparent to the incoming sunlight, are almost opaque to the outgoing infra-red. These are

34

water-vapour and carbon dioxide, which make up approximately 2 per cent and 3 hundredths of a per cent respectively of the whole atmosphere. . . .

We live in fact in a gigantic greenhouse, the glass of which is replaced by the water vapour and carbon dioxide of the atmosphere.

Water vapour

The water vapour in the atmosphere comes mainly from the evaporation of sea-water under the hot sun of the tropics. It is invisible, like any other gas or vapour, unless it is condensed to form droplets, either as cloud or rain. And now comes the crucial point, namely that it can only condense on small material particles already floating in the air: particles of sea-salt thrown up from the sea as spray, and carried by rising currents high into the atmosphere; or fine dust from volcanoes; or meteoric dust from outside the earth's atmosphere.

Thus the total amount of water vapour held in the atmosphere depends on a delicate equilibrium between the rate of its evaporation from the earth's surface and the rate at which it is deposited on condensation nuclei in the atmosphere, to be returned to the earth as rain or snow. Condensed in the form of clouds, which may either disperse once more into invisible vapour or jettison their cargo as rain, the water content of the atmosphere has a profound influence on the balance between the incoming sunlight and the outgoing infra-red emission from the earth's surface, apart altogether from its greenhouse effect—acting indeed in the opposite direction; for nearly half of the incoming sunlight is reflected directly back into space by the cloud-cover of the earth.

Cloud-patterns

Cloud formations in the atmosphere are clearly a challenge to the meteorologists. Not only does the overall cloud-cover help to determine the earth's climate, but its ever-changing pattern has a major influence on the world's weather. So far, a complete picture of the total instantaneous cloud-pattern has been quite impossible. Photographs taken from high-flying rockets have given fragmentary records, at quite arbitrary intervals of time, of the cloud-formations over limited areas of the earth's surface, chiefly in the United States. But an overall picture must await the full development of artificial satellites, which can orbit the earth from Pole to Pole for months on end, recording the kaleidoscopic changes in the cloud-pattern over the entire globe.

Glaciers again

Far aloft, say above 20,000 feet, there are normally no centres of condensation of water vapour, such as exist nearer the earth's surface. But there is still, even at these high altitudes, a considerable proportion of water vapour. Here is where meteoric dust from outer space could play an important part. Thus recent studies have suggested that there is a marked tendency for a world-wide increase in rainfall to follow the impact on the earth's atmosphere of certain regularly occurring meteor showers. One quite serious speculation on past glacial epochs has, indeed, focused on the possibility that the earth may have run into the debris of broken planets, which could cause condensation of the water vapour held in the higher levels of the atmosphere, with a consequent increase in rainfall; and following on that, a decrease in the water-vapour greenhouse effect sufficient to lower the whole temperature of the earth, to the point of glaciation in the tropics. This theory is, indeed, the current rival to that considered in the preceding chapter, which would explain the record of glaciation near the Equator, not necessarily as arising from a general lowering of the surface temperature, but from polar wandering, or continental drift, or a combination of both.

Carbon dioxide

Now let us look at the second minor constituent of the atmosphere which is important to the radiation balance of the earth—carbon dioxide. Here there are theories which for example would explain the lush vegetation of past geological ages in Greenland by the existence of the very active volcanoes of that period, which might have belched forth enough carbon dioxide to increase the greenhouse effect to the point where the overall temperature of the earth was sufficiently high to induce tropical conditions in the sub-Arctic. The polar wanderers, on the other hand, say: "Not a bit of it: Greenland was once near the Equator!". . . .

Only a closer study both of glaciation and of polar wandering can decide this issue.

Man-made climate

There is a stimulating prospect ahead of us: that mankind is quite unwittingly altering the overall climate of the earth, by spewing carbon dioxide into the atmosphere in ever-increasing quantities, from factory chimneys, industrial plants, and car exhausts. At the moment, something like 10 billion tons of CO_2 per annum are being poured into the atmosphere from man-made engines, as against a total atmospheric content of rather less than 3 trillion tons. By the end of the present century, we may expect an annual increase of around 50 billion tons.

This is an amount sufficient to affect the radiation balance of the earth. The greenhouse effect of the increased percentage of CO_2 in the atmosphere must be expected to raise the overall temperature. The consequences are cumulative, however: first, the warmed-up oceans will have to part with some of their dissolved carbon dioxide, which will result in their getting still warmer; so second, they begin to evaporate larger quantities of water vapour. The nett result is an enhanced H_2O–cum–CO_2 greenhouse effect, which could melt the polar ice-caps, so that London, Paris, and New York would all be inundated with salt sea-water. Scientists are already thinking seriously of ways of keeping track of this man-made phenomenon, so as to be able to predict what the future has in store.

Water vapour and the winds of heaven

The water vapour in the atmosphere plays a dual rôle. It is a factor in maintaining the stability of the earth's climate; but it acts also as the fuel of the atmospheric heat engine that drives the winds.

It is well known that to raise steam in a domestic kettle, or a railway engine, or a steam turbine, we have not only to heat the water to the boiling point, but to pump in additional energy—the so-called latent heat of vaporisation—in order to convert the boiling water to steam at the same temperature. In a steam engine it is the release of this latent heat in the cycle of evaporation and condensation that is the source of energy that drives its moving parts.

So also in the cycle of evaporation and condensation of water vapour in the atmosphere. The water vapour evaporated from the earth's surface carries its latent heat of vaporisation locked up in it into the air, to be released when the vapour condenses as cloud, or falls as rain, hail, or snow. The moving parts of the atmospheric heat engine are the winds, and the energy behind all the winds of the world is enormous, equal to that which would be released by the explosion of some 10 million atomic bombs.

The age of sail

The world pattern of the surface winds was well established by the end of the eighteenth century. The master mariners of

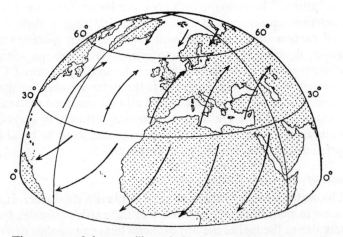

The pattern of the prevailing winds at the earth's surface, which has been known for at least a hundred years.

the age of sail knew how to take advantage of the easterly trades; the grain-ships of Australia ran before the westerly roaring forties round Cape Horn; ships could lie becalmed for weeks in the doldrums of the Equator.

Throughout the nineteenth century the meteorologists built up a model of the general circulation of the atmosphere, based on the known pattern of the surface winds. This model pictured a circulation in three compartments, or cells, in each hemisphere, predominantly in the direction of the earth's meridians.

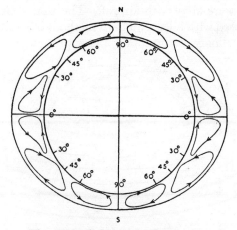

The outmoded model of the general circulation of the atmosphere, made in an attempt to account for the surface winds.

The transport of warm air from the tropics towards the Poles, and of cold air from the Poles towards the Equator, required of any model of the atmospheric heat engine, was accounted for. The model was in agreement with the evidence for a strong descending air motion in the region of the horse latitudes. There was, however, an inherent difficulty about the middle cell, since here the postulated circulation required the slow transport of the air aloft from higher to lower latitudes, that is, against the natural trend followed in the equatorial and polar cells; so that it would need a constant supply of energy from other parts of the atmosphere for its maintenance.

The age of air travel

The past few decades have seen the development of air travel to the point where a knowledge of the winds aloft has become as necessary to navigation as of the sea winds in the days of sail.

So far, the acquisition of this new knowledge has been confined chiefly to the northern hemisphere, vastly accelerated by the demands of the Second World War, when bombers shuttled across the Atlantic at heights of 30,000 feet, and the skies above the Pacific were alive with aircraft. The upper air was intensively explored with all the modern methods of wind determination: free balloons, radio-sonde, radar probes.

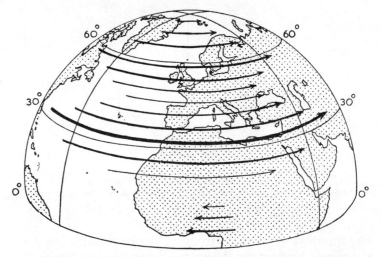

The pattern of the winds aloft which the air age has revealed.

The results were startling. Here was no stately meridianal circulation, such as had been pictured in the nineteenth-century models. Instead, the new search revealed a pattern of strong westerly winds aloft, right down to below latitude 30°, where there is a change-over to high level easterlies. More than that, these high-level westerlies showed two sharp maxima: a relatively stable maximum high up above the surface calms of the horse latitudes; and another maximum, fluctuating in strength and mobile in latitude, according to the seasons and the lower-level weather conditions, marking the boundary of the so-

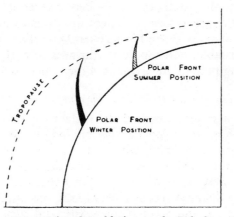

The polar front, separating the cold air over the Pole from the warm air of the tropics, changes its position with the seasons. So also does the polar front jet stream, which flows high up under the roof of the troposphere.

called polar front, that separates the cold air-mass over the Pole from the warm air of the sub-tropics.

The jet streams

These maxima in the westerlies aloft are the jet streams, concentrated rivers of air, a couple of hundred miles wide and 2 or 3 miles deep, lashing around the world at speeds of up to 200 miles an hour. They flow right up under the roof of the troposphere, and indeed there is evidence that they may pierce the roof, allowing an exchange between the turbulent air of the troposphere and the comparatively calm air of the stratosphere that had never previously been suspected.

All this, of course, refers to the northern hemisphere: but already evidence is accumulating that a similar pattern of high-level westerlies holds for the southern hemisphere also. But possibly with an important difference. . . .

The map of the earth is not symmetrical, as between the northern and southern hemispheres. Over the North Pole we have the flat ice of the polar sea, over the South Pole the high-lying plateau of the Antarctic Continent; in the middle latitudes of the northern hemisphere, large land-masses; in comparable latitudes in the southern hemisphere the equalising watery wastes of the great oceans. There are already hints that the enormous air-mass which hovers over Antarctica may suddenly become unstable, and topple northwards in a gigantic shock-wave through the middle regions of the upper atmosphere.

The problem of global circulation in the atmosphere

The air age has presented the meteorologists with a pretty problem: how to reconcile the predominantly north–south trend of the surface winds with such a purely zonal circulation aloft. Or, put in another way, we have this question: How can a whirl of westerly winds above the Poles, such as has been revealed by the most recent observations, successfully transport warm air from the tropics polewards, and vice versa, as is demanded by the fact that the tropics do not become progressively hotter, and the Poles progressively cooler?

We can only answer this question with any certainty at the present moment for the northern hemisphere: and there it is now quite certain that the exchange of tropical warm air and polar cold air does *not* happen as the result of a smooth, regular circulatory process, but as the product of a sporadic exchange of hot and cold parcels of air across the polar front. Only in the trade-wind belt, the region between the Equator and 30° north and south, does the traditional meridianal circulation—cold air at the surface streaming towards the Equator, warm air aloft drifting north and south—still hold good under the lens of modern examination.

Fuelling the atmospheric heat engine

The trade-wind belt is an important fuelling station for the atmospheric heat engine, with the trade-wind clouds, growing ever larger as they approach the Equator, as the fuel pumps.

The trade-wind clouds are launched in the air above the warm sub-tropical seas of the horse latitudes, where the evaporation of water vapour is a maximum. In the northern hemisphere they set sail southwards from the Bermudas, driven before a wind that blows from the belt of dry air at high pressure, which has come down from below the sub-tropical jet stream aloft, towards the region of low pressure at the Equator, where warm moist air is rising. Gradually they alter course, from due south to south-west; for they are running before a wind that has to obey the deflecting force of the spinning earth. Indeed, neither the trade-winds nor their moisture-carrying clouds would ever reach the Equator were it not for the frictional drag of the earth's surface: the trades would swing hard to the right, to become winds blowing around the globe from east to west—and their cargo of water vapour would never be delivered.

Studies of these tall chimney-shaped clouds from aircraft have shown that they are in a constant state of growth to windward and decay down wind, or at times vice versa, and that there is a turbulent circulation within each cloud which makes it act as a powerful water-vapour pump, with the intake near sea level and the output at levels as high as 7,000 feet. In their passage to the Equator, the trade-wind clouds inject enormous quantities of water vapour, night and day, into the ever warmer air-stream of the trades.

Arrived at the Equator, the warm, moist air from the north converges with the trade-winds of the southern hemisphere, and is swept aloft, carrying the clouds with it. In the ascent to the cold regions of the upper troposphere, the water vapour is jettisoned, to fall in sheets of tropical rain on land and sea below. At the same time, the solar energy it has held entrapped as latent heat during its journey south is released, to drive the whole wind system. . . .

The belt of upper easterlies drifts north from the Equator, in a complex pattern of swirls and eddies, impelled by the earth's deflecting force; until immediately below the sub-tropical jet stream, which marks the upper edge of the boundary from which the surface westerlies of the high latitudes and the sub-tropical easterlies diverge, cold dry air descends to ground level, growing always denser and warmer as it sinks. The trade-wind cycle is complete.

Repaying a debt to the earth

The easterly trade-winds flow partly against the direction of rotation of the earth, which is of course from west to east. As we have seen, it is the friction between the moving air and the earth's surface which holds the trades on their oblique course towards the Equator. In their passage over sea and land, therefore, these winds steal some of the rotational momentum of the spinning earth. This stolen momentum must somehow be paid back, otherwise the whole circulation of the air would grind to a stop. How is this achieved?

The process is a subtle one, and has only recently been properly understood. Let us look first at the prevailing westerlies, which flow pole-ward from the zone of the horse latitudes in either hemisphere. These winds are moving partly in the direction of rotation of the earth; hence they *part* with some of their own momentum in their passage pole-ward. It then turns out that the areas of the earth's surface covered by the easterlies and the westerlies are such that the momentum gained by the easterlies is just balanced by that lost by the westerlies. You could say, in fact, that this is why the surface winds are what they are! But now the easterlies and westerlies must somehow exchange momentum, so that the balance is held for the whole system of earth and atmosphere. This can only happen by the turbulent mixing of air eddies, flowing clockwise and counter-clockwise, across the boundary between the two systems. . . And now comes the dramatic conclusion: for a rather abstruse mathematical calculation shows that theoretically this turbulent mixing is most strongly favoured across a boundary where the increase of wind velocity from the ground upwards is greatest. This is of course precisely the case in latitudes 30° north and south, where we have the calms of the horse latitudes at sea-level, and the sub-tropical jet-streams flowing under the roof of the troposphere directly above them!

Pole-ward of 30° north and south

Now comes the problem of the mechanism of the global circulation of the atmosphere pole-ward of the horse latitudes.

Only in the northern hemisphere has observation of the higher levels of the troposphere progressed far enough properly to discuss this question: and so all that follows refers solely to the north polar cap, from the Pole southwards to latitude 30° north: although, as has been remarked, there is already evi-

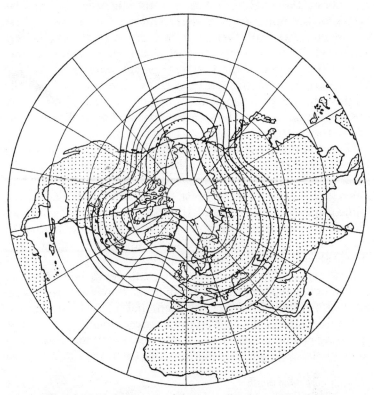

The circumpolar vortex of the upper level westerly winds.

dence that similar conditions hold in the southern hemisphere. Here it can be said at once that some degree of meridianal circulation, such as we have described for the trade-wind cell, is only possible south of the polar front: northwards of the front lies a whirl of westerly winds, bounded aloft by the polar front jet-stream. The middle cell of the traditional picture shrinks to a mere 5° or 10° of latitude, southward of the polar front jet-stream.

The circumpolar vortex

Northward of the polar front, between say 10,000 and 30,000 feet above the earth's surface, lies the gigantic circumpolar vortex of the upper-level westerly winds. The speed of these winds increases with height above ground: at 30,000 feet the speed of the circumpolar westerlies is perhaps three times that at the bottom of the vortex. And underneath the roof of the troposphere, at the southern rim of the vortex, flows the mighty aerial river of the polar-front jet-stream, in whose centre the winds roar around the world at speeds of 200 miles an hour or even more.

Charts of the winds of the circumpolar whirl, made at an intermediate level of say 15,000 or 20,000 feet, show that the polar front is scalloped into great waves, measuring as much as 4,000 miles from crest to crest. This whole wave-system is found to be careering round the Pole from west to east, although at times it may become stationary for a brief period, or even start to veer backwards. The winds themselves, however, streak always predominately from west to east.

Now the *amplitude* of these waves, the depth between crest and trough, varies enormously with time. Sometimes the waves are shallow, sometimes they are deep: and all the time the waxing and waning of their aerial surge is accompanied by a corresponding erratic meander of the jet-stream aloft and of a variations in the weather conditions at the earth's surface.

Cut-offs north and south

At intervals which are meantime quite unpredictable, the amplitude of the waves of the circumpolar whirl, and of the lashings of the jet-stream aloft, may increase to the extent that the troughs of the waves extend far south above the sub-tropics, while the crests thrust north into the polar regions. In this unstable condition of the polar vortex, cold dry air from the polar cap slides southward in the troughs, warm moist air from the tropics rides northward on the crests. And now the wave motion, and the lashing of the jet above, become so violent that great circular eddies of cold air may be thrown off from the boundary of the circumpolar whirl into the south,

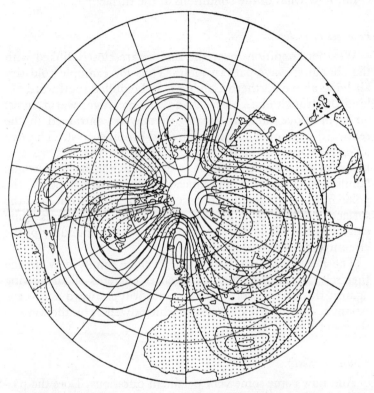

Violent meandering of the winds aloft, bounded at the highest levels by the polar front jet-stream, leads to cut-offs of warm and cold air masses north and south of the polar front.

while swirls of warm air are enmeshed in the polar vortex, far north of the polar front. Thereafter, the jet-stream swings back onto its normal course, and the great waves on the polar front shrink once again to a more normal amplitude. The whole cycle of expansion and contraction of the circumpolar whirl lasts about a month or six weeks.

It is in this untidy way, therefore, that the exchange of hot

and cold air between the sub-tropics and the polar regions,
so necessary to the maintenance of the overall radiation balance
of the earth, is accomplished. . . .

But now what of the conditions at the surface?

Families of cyclones

Weather conditions near the surface are closely linked with
the changing wave-pattern aloft. Thus for example cold dry
air lying above northern Canada may be pulled southward behind the trough of an eastward-advancing wave; warm, moist
air from above the Caribbean Sea may be entrained in the
rearward edge of the next northward-probing crest. The two
air-masses meet in a turbulent struggle on the western sea-
board of the Atlantic: and it is then that the birth of whole
families of cyclones is announced on the lower slopes of the
polar front. Significantly, the sector of the polar front near the
surface, covered by a family of cyclones, corresponds quite
closely to the whole depth of the wave on the boundary of the
circumpolar vortex aloft.

The individual members of the cyclone family now detach
themselves from the front, as circular currents of air flowing
against the direction of the clock, and drift eastward across the
Atlantic, causing the depressions which dwellers on the western
shores of Europe know so well.

Cause or effect?

And now come some very pertinent questions: Does the pattern of the winds aloft control the weather conditions at the
surface? Is the jet-stream Prospero commanding, or obedient
Ariel running on the sharp wind of the north?

To answer these questions is rather like trying to decide
whether the angle between the arms of a centrifugal governor
is determined by the speed of the engine, or vice versa. The
truth of the matter is that the whole atmosphere is subject to an
extremely tight feed-back control, whereby any single event in
the troposphere influences every other, and is itself influenced
by all these events in return. It is this fact which makes the

study of the overall atmospheric circulation at once so difficult and so fascinating.

Even if the picture of the global circulation which is now beginning to emerge were complete, this close interdependence of all atmospheric phenomena, all over the earth, would make the prediction from the current situation of future conditions in any one area—long-range weather prediction, in fact—impossible without the aid of ultra-rapid electronic computers—"giant brains"—which can handle just such complex feed-back systems in a way that no human computer can begin to attempt. It is an interesting thought that the development of our knowledge of the atmosphere on the one hand, and of the calculating machines on the other, are converging at this very moment to the point where the machines can be fed with sufficient data to give a correct answer! Meteorology is indeed on the brink of a new era.

The next phase

Before the next steps can be taken towards a more complete understanding of the global circulation of the atmosphere, on which really reliable long-range weather forecasting must depend, there is a whole range of questions that have to be decided. . . . Thus in the northern hemisphere, about which we know most, the meteorologists are still baffled about how much of the circulation depends on the zonal movement of the winds aloft, with the sporadic exchange of warm and cold air-masses across the polar front, and how much on meridianal circulation, particularly in the region south of the polar front and north of the horse latitudes. In the southern hemisphere there is still the need to verify the evidence of jet-streams aloft, comparable to those that the air age has revealed north of the Equator. There is the need to check back on the existence of a circumpolar whirl over the South Pole, such as we have come to recognise over the north polar cap. There is the urge to investigate the conditions above the Antarctic Continent, to trace the presence or absence of the shock-waves that may spread north from its unstable air-cap. There is the open question of the interchange of air north and south across the Equator. There are the

numerical checks, even in the better-known northern hemisphere, of the transport pole-ward and Equator-ward of energy,
of momentum, and of water vapour. . . .

And, finally, there is the necessity of determining how far the
climate and weather of the world depends on the inter-reaction
of the atmosphere and the oceans.

CHAPTER 3

CURRENTS, WAVES AND TIDES

THE oceans cover 147 million square miles of the earth's total surface of 197 million square miles. Geographically, this vast expanse of water has been very thoroughly explored. The surface currents of the oceans have been charted; the depths of the seas bordering the land have been carefully sounded; tide tables give exact information to shipping entering all the harbours of the world. Yet the scientific exploration of the oceans is still only in its preliminary stages.

Why do the surface currents run with the strength, and in the position, that geographical exploration finds them? How are the deep-sea currents formed? How can we trace the origin and mechanism of the long waves that may cross an ocean to wreck the shipping in harbours on the far side? Why are the tides so different in different parts of the world, with twice-daily tides having a range of 40 to 50 feet in the Bay of Fundy in Nova Scotia, and only a few feet on the shores of many oceanic islands?

Ocean gyres

Every yachtsman has seen the cats' paws that the wind sends streaking over the surface of lake or sea. In such a way, through the drag of the wind on the sea, the surface currents of the oceans are born of the great wind-systems of the earth. This fact has been known in an empirical way since the days of sail; but only in the last few years has the uniform pattern of the surface currents of the oceans of the world been satisfactorily explained.

If we look at a world map of the ocean currents, we see a consistent picture of clockwise circulation in the ocean basins of the northern hemisphere, of counter-clockwise circulation in the southern hemisphere. But the circulation is not symmetrical: it is strongest on the western shores of the oceans.

We recognise the Gulf Stream in the North Atlantic, the Brazil
Current in the South Atlantic, the Kuroshio Current off Japan

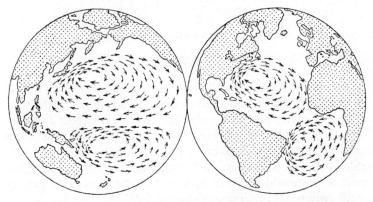

The main current systems in the land-locked basins are displaced
westwards by the spin of the earth.

in the northern Pacific. What is the origin of this uniform
pattern?

These surface-current systems are, as we might expect, linked
with those of the prevailing winds. Thus in the familiar Atlantic

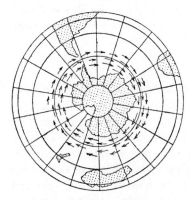

The Antarctic Current flows right
round the world before the prevailing winds.

we recognise immediately the trace of the easterly trades in the
south and of the prevailing westerlies in the north. But now look
at the Antarctic Current, driven by the roaring forties from
west to east, and see how it goes right around the world in the

southern latitudes, where there are no land barriers in its path. We begin to realise that the ocean gyres, as they are called, are brought about by the fact that the principal oceans of the world are land-locked. Moreover, these land barriers are partly responsible for the westward displacement of the gyres.

The full explanation of the westward displacement of the ocean gyres is a rather subtle one, and only a bare outline of the argument can be given here. Pin-pointing our attention on the North Atlantic, we see a continuous clockwise circulation of the surface currents, born of the prevailing winds. This motion of the surface water is retarded by friction between water and land at the sides of the basin. If the forward urge of the winds and the backward drag of the edge friction were the only forces involved, the water circulation would be symmetrical about the centre of the ocean. But the spin of the earth, acting on the freely moving water, increases the clockwise circulation in the west, where the water is flowing north, and reduces it in the east where the water is flowing south. A balanced circulation can only be maintained, therefore, if the edge friction is greater in the west than in the east; and this is achieved by the presence of a stronger and narrower current in the west.

Exactly the same arguments may be applied to the other major ocean-current systems. In other words, the broad picture has been painted; but the details—why the Gulf Stream, for example, meanders in its course, why it is filamented in its structure, with fast-flowing fibriles imbedded in slower currents—these details have still to be determined.

Deep-sea currents

The conventional picture of the formation of the deep-sea currents is one of surface waters, made heavy either by being cold, or by their saltiness, or both, sinking until they find a level that matches their own density, when they spread out horizontally below to form a hidden current.

There is of course no doubt that this process is part of the picture. But there is now considerable evidence that the surface winds play an important rôle in initiating circulation of the oceans at great depths. One way in which the surface winds can influence the deep-sea currents depends on the same fact as we have already invoked to account for the ocean gyres at the surface—the ocean basins are not limitless, but are hemmed in by land boundaries. This means that water can be piled up by surface winds against a coast until the column of water so formed can exert strong horizontal pressure at great depths.

The question is still open: How much do these two such different trends contribute to the observed circulation in the deeper reaches of the oceans? The answer must await not only a better knowledge of the effects of the surface winds on the motion of the waters in the ocean basins, but also of fuller observation of the actual movements of the deep-sea currents.

Our present knowledge of the deep-sea currents is mainly qualitative. The trouble is that they move so extremely slowly. Thus the bottom water of the Atlantic, moving north from the boundaries of Antarctica, creeps northwards at a rate of not more than a couple of inches per second, so that it takes something like 20 years for it to reach the Equator.

Attempts have been made to trace the creep of these deep-sea currents by means of "carbon dating", which has proved so spectacularly successful in archæological research. This method depends on the fact that a special species of carbon— carbon with atomic weight 14 as against the normal atomic weight of 12—is formed in small amounts in the atmosphere as the result of the bombardment of the nitrogen molecules by cosmic rays from outer space. This "Carbon Fourteen" is radioactive, with a rate of decay which reduces its initial radioactivity by one half in approximately 5,500 years. It enters the sea as dissolved carbon dioxide, and so a measurement of the radioactivity of the carbon present in a sample of sea-water taken from a deep ocean current should tell us how long it has been travelling from its point of origin at the surface. This method gives a period of as long as 2,000 years for the passage of Antarctic water to the Equator, which is wildly different from the conventional estimates.

Clearly there is much work to be done before a quantitative knowledge of the deep ocean currents is ours. New methods are being devised, however, by which direct measurement of these hidden currents should become possible on a world-wide scale, as we shall see later in Chapter 8.

The anatomy of the Atlantic

An idea of the complexity of the problem can be gained by considering the qualitative picture of the deep-water circulation of the Atlantic, the ocean which has been most intensively studied up to the present.

First, there is a northward flow of surface water from the northern reaches of the Antarctic Ocean, which slips down below the warmer surface currents of the South Atlantic gyre, to edge across the Equator at an average depth of 2,000 feet, mixing with other water-masses until it loses its identity in the North Atlantic, around latitude 20° north.

Second, there is a flow of very salt water from the Mediterranean. In this all-but-inland sea, sparsely fed with fresh water by its rivers or from its light rainfall, the burnished sun evaporates more water from the surface than can be replenished by river and rain combined. Surface water from the Atlantic, therefore, comes streaming in through the Straits of Gibraltar to make up the deficit, while the heavy, salt-laden Mediterranean water spills out over the submerged sill, 150 fathoms below the surface of the Straits, into the open ocean. There it cascades downwards through the Atlantic waters to a depth of 3,000 to 6,000 feet, then fans out as far as Greenland in the north, the Bermudas to the south-west, and southwards of the Equator.

Below this level again, at depths of around 10,000 feet, is a flow of very cold salt water, southward from its place of origin off the south-east coast of Greenland. Here, at the surface, cold water flowing out of the North Polar Sea meets and mingles with the warm waters of the Gulf Stream, which have come north heavily laden with salt. The resulting mixture, now both cold and salty, sinks in enormous quantities, to find its level deep below the surface, where it edges southward right across the Equator.

And finally there is the bottom water from Antarctica, which is very salt and dense, since the freezing ice of the Antarctic

Ocean leaves the salts behind in the water. This cold, heavy water slides down the sloping shelf which surrounds the Antarctic Continent, then creeps northwards over the ocean floor, until it mixes with the waters above it in the North Atlantic.

Long waves

Waves with a periodic motion more rapid than the ordinary wind swell and slower than the tides are currently the subject of intensive study. With periods lying between 5 and 60 minutes, they are difficult to observe, they are of many varieties, and their causes are often obscure.

The classic example of a long wave is of course the tsunami, or tidal wave, which results from an earthquake on the ocean floor. But it appears that marked oscillations of sea-level on the coasts around the southern seas may also come from a tropical cyclone far out in the open ocean, which, reacting on the surface of the water below, forms the centre of a disturbance which sends long waves radiating out from it in all directions.

On any coast which lies open to one of the great oceans of the world, "surf-beats" may be observed: oscillations with a period of around 5 minutes which accompany the ocean swell arriving from a distant wind area. These slow oscillations may cause considerable confusion, and even damage, to shipping in a harbour in which the natural period of oscillation of the water is close to that of the surf-beats.

Storm-surges which can cause severe coastal flooding occur in the shallower seas, if a surge from the open ocean is intensified by winds near the coast.

These, then, are some of the phenomena associated with long waves. They have been studied chiefly at stations on the edge of the great continents, where the presence of a sloping shelf between the geographical boundaries of the continents and the deep sea beyond is a complicating factor. Indeed, the proper place to make a scientific study of long waves is at stations situated on small islands in mid-ocean. And this will be done for the first time, in a really systematic way, during the International Geophysical Year.

Ocean tides

So long as the ocean floor was pictured as a great flat plain, the curious diversity of tidal motions in different areas of the globe were quite inexplicable.

The invention of the supersonic echo-sounder changed the whole observational situation, radically and permanently. Where previously the sounding of the depth of water in the ocean had been a laborious business of line and sinker, readily applicable only to the shallow seas, the echo-sounder, carried on ocean-going survey vessels, now brings back soundings of the deepest ocean basins faster than they can be entered on the charts.

The results have shown that the floor of the ocean, far from being flat, has a topography even bolder than that of the continents. The echo-sounder has revealed great mountain chains, deep trenches, yawning canyons on the ocean bottom. There is the mid-Atlantic ridge, an enormous range of mountains stretching from off Greenland in the north to Ascension Island in the south; there are the recently discovered mid-Pacific mountains, rearing up from the bottom to heights of 10,000 feet and more, lying between Hawaii and the Marshal Islands; there are the abyssal depths of the Philippine trench, or the Japan trench, great gashes in the ocean bottom, 30,000 feet deep in parts. Only the floor of the Indian Ocean appears so far to be really flat: a vast plain of black basaltic rock, so smooth that the echo-sounder records the rise and fall of the survey vessel on the ocean swell, rather than any irregularities in the featureless ocean bottom.

Thus the oceans must now be thought of as divided into a number of separate basins, the water in which has each its own natural rate of rocking about a central dead point, or node: both from end to end and from side to side of its own basin. It is not so surprising, therefore, that the tidal motions in different localities should vary so markedly in extent and type. At the one extreme there must come the case where a natural period of oscillation of the water in the basin coincides more or less closely with the rhythm of the pull exerted by the sun and moon: here we have strong, well-defined tides, as in the Bay of Fundy. Or at the other extreme we have the case of an island lying close to a dead point or node of the natural oscillation, when we should expect such small tides as actually exist off certain oceanic islands. As time goes on, we may look for an even closer correlation between the shapes of the ocean basins and their tidal behaviour, although the analysis of the complicated motions of the water in the basins is by no means an easy matter.

Changes in sea-level

Accurate measurements of mean sea-level are of the utmost importance, not only to navigators, but also to the engineers who are responsible for harbour works, coastal protection, and the like. We can, of course, speak only of *mean* sea-level, for apart from the rise and fall of the tides, there are variations in sea-level arising from a number of quite different causes. Thus the gyres in the ocean, with which we began, themselves give rise to sloping surfaces on the face of the sea. In the North Atlantic, for example, the surface of the sea slopes up quite sharply from the eastern boundary of the Gulf Stream towards the middle of the North Atlantic gyre, thanks to the spin of the earth. Then again there are oscillations of sea-level in the equatorial Pacific, having a period of around four days, which seem to coincide with variations of a similar period in the equatorial wind system.

There is no doubt that mean sea-level varies over the seasons of the year, and that these variations are world-wide phenomena. Careful analysis has shown that the seasonal changes in most parts of the world may be accounted for by the simple expansion and contraction of sea-water under the varying heat of the sun, so that the change in sea-level is due to a change in the volume of the water rather than in its absolute amount.

In polar latitudes, however, there are indications that the actual amount of water varies with the seasons, and in a remarkably interesting way. There appears to be more water in the northern seas in the northern spring than in the northern fall, and a corresponding excess in the southern hemisphere in the southern spring. Is this particular seasonal rhythm to be accounted for by an increased contribution of water from the surrounding land-masses in the appropriate spring season, or is there an annual movement of water to and fro across the Equator? We know too little as yet about the waters off the coasts of Antarctica to answer this question with confidence, one way or the other. It is a matter for further study.

CHAPTER 4

PATTERNS IN THE OUTER ATMOSPHERE

A study in solar control

THE circulation in the thin sheath of the atmosphere nearest the earth's surface—10 to 20 miles in thickness—is, as we have seen, powered by the sun.

Indirectly, however. The global circulation of the air in the lower atmosphere, the sweep of the ocean currents, the phases of the world's weather, all come from the unequal warming of the earth's surface by the sun's radiation, rather than from a direct influence of the sun on the lower atmosphere itself. Hence the difficulty of disentangling cause and effect in a description of wind and weather: so that we may be equally right in asserting that the winds give rise to the Gulf Stream, or that the Gulf Stream makes the trade-winds.

In the outer atmosphere, high above cloud level and the blanketing effect of water vapour and carbon dioxide, the control of the sun on the behaviour of the earth's envelope of air becomes progressively more direct. There are many reasons for this new state of affairs: among others, because re-radiation of the sun's energy from the earth becomes less and less important; because the air, although its basic composition is essentially much the same as at the earth's surface, becomes more and more rarefied; but also because the short-wave radiation from the sun, falling on the molecules of the constituent gases, is always less filtered of its shortest wave-lengths as height above earth increases.

The energy in a light-wave is carried in separate packets, or *quanta*, which are the larger the shorter the wave-length. The effect on a molecule of air of the ultra-violet light impinging on it in the higher levels of the atmosphere is therefore quite similar to that of a bombardment by a stream of particles—light-particles, or photons. Under this bombardment, a molecule—say of oxygen—may split up, or dissociate, into two atoms. And if the oxygen atoms in their turn are bombarded by light quanta of shorter wave-length and still higher energy, an electron may be knocked clean out of the atom, leaving the atom positively charged, or *ionised*.

These two processes are known respectively as photo-dissociation and photo-ionisation. We should expect to find that photo-ionisation is possible only in the higher reaches of the outer atmosphere, where the shortest ultra-violet waves from the sun have not yet been filtered out; and that photo-dissociation occurs throughout the whole height of the atmosphere, to become the predominant factor at the lower levels. This is in fact precisely what we find: between 20 and 50 miles above the earth's surface the most interesting components of the atmosphere are the bits and pieces of molecules which result from the bombardment of the less energetic light quanta; between 50 and 200 miles up we find that free electrons and positive ions decide the characteristics of the upper atmosphere.

This very direct solar control of the upper atmosphere leads to the imprint of regular variations on its behaviour, which all stem from the motion of the earth around the sun, or from rhythms in the sun itself. Thus there are daily variations in the properties of the upper atmosphere, arising from the earth's rotation; there are seasonal variations, following the earth's motion in its orbit; there are 27-day recurrences, in tune with the sun's own rotation; and there are 11-year cycles corresponding to the cycle of the sun's eruptive activity. In short, a study of the outer atmosphere tells us much about the sun; and observation of the sun gives us many clues about the nature of the outer atmosphere.

The chemistry of the outer atmosphere

Any study of the outer atmosphere must begin with an examination of its composition. We can say at once that the basic composition of the atmosphere—four parts nitrogen to one of oxygen—remains much the same up to a height of at least 120 miles, although the air becomes always more rarefied as we

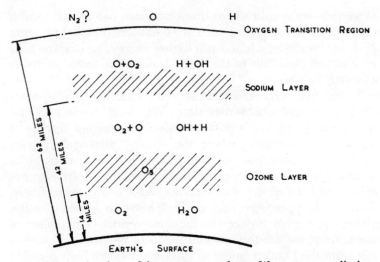

The strange chemistry of the upper atmosphere. Water vapour splits into atomic hydrogen (H) and hydroxyl (OH); oxygen splits into its constituent atoms; ozone is formed in a quite well-defined layer; and sodium atoms are also found.

ascend. But we shall find in the upper reaches of the earth's atmosphere a number of molecular species, products of the sun's chemistry, some of which are quite surprising.

Oxygen

Oxygen plays a most important part in the chemistry of the upper atmosphere, and a vital rôle in conditioning life on earth as we know it: which is all the more remarkable when we remember that some of the free oxygen in the atmosphere is a product of life itself.

The oxygen we breathe at sea-level is molecular oxygen— O_2. Samples of air taken from levels 5, 10, 20, 40 miles above earth would, however, show gradually less and less molecular oxygen, and more and more of the atomic oxygen —O— born of the bombardment of the molecules by the ultra-violet light of the sun: until above 60 miles high, quite abruptly, the predominant component would be atomic oxygen.

In the ascent, moreover, a third species of oxygen appears—

namely ozone, the three-atom variety O_3. Ozone is formed by collisions between O_2 and O, and largely destroyed by subsequent collisions with atomic oxygen: $O_3 + O = 2O_2$. So inevitably there must come a level in the upper air where there is enough atomic oxygen to favour the formation of ozone, but not too much to make it impossible for the ozone to survive. Such a level is indeed found, at around 10 to 20 miles above earth, where there lies a quite sharply defined ozone layer.

Ozone

The total quantity of ozone in the ozone layer is quite small. Thus although it is over 10 miles in thickness, up there 15 miles above the earth's surface, it would shrink to a skin of only about a tenth of an inch if compressed to the same density as the air at sea-level. Yet it is of extreme importance.

In the first place, it is a potent absorber of the lethal ultra-violet radiation from the sun; it is in fact oxygen, in the form of ozone in the ozone layer, and not only the oxygen we breathe, that makes life possible. A vivid impression of this property of the ozone layer is got by taking photographs of the sun's spectrum from a rocket shot up through it: in the picture facing page 156 we see how the range of radiation received by a spectroscope carried in the nose of the rocket races into the ultra-violet as the rocket penetrates the layer.

But the ozone layer also absorbs strongly in the infra-red. It therefore adds to the greenhouse effect of the water vapour and carbon dioxide present in the troposphere, so influencing the radiation balance of the earth, and hence in turn the world's weather. In fact, it is beginning to appear that a detailed knowledge of the ozone layer may be of considerable importance to weather prediction. Already we know that the amount of ozone in the ozone layer varies by night and day, and with the seasons, which indeed it must do by the very sun-controlled mechanism of its formation. This means, however, that the distribution of ozone in its spherical shell is not regular, but patchy; and the resulting movements pole-wards and towards the Equator within the shell are still not properly understood.

Sodium

The formation of an ozone layer in the upper atmosphere is, as we have seen, both explainable and expected. But above the ozone layer, at about 50 miles above earth, there is a tenuous layer of gaseous metallic sodium whose origin is a complete mystery.

The sodium in the sodium layer reveals itself to the spectrocopes of observers on earth by the familiar yellow light that the atoms emit, under bombardment by electrons or photons, such as can be seen on many a strip-lighted highway in and around our cities. The sodium vapour of the street-lamp is, of course, excited to emit the yellow light by an electrical discharge within the lamp; but it can also be excited, if we wish, by irradiating it with light of just the right yellow wave-length.

The second method is the one responsible for the twilight glow from the sodium layer in the upper atmosphere, which is detectable with the aid of sensitive optical instruments. And the source of the exciting radiation is the sun! The light from the sodium layer is invisible by day, against the background of bright sunlight; but at twilight the yellow line flashes out in the waiting spectroscopes—signals from excited sodium atoms on the sun, re-laid by the resonance radiation of sodium atoms in the earth's outer atmosphere.

We have spoken of the sodium layer as tenuous. There is in fact in all only about a ton of sodium vapour aloft, equivalent to one atom of sodium in a million million other atmospheric particles. Yet so sensitive are its atoms to excitation that the yellow light they emit is not only sufficient to reveal their presence, but also to hint to observers on earth that the atmosphere at the height of the sodium layer is not the calm aerial ocean we might expect, but is torn by great winds.

So the next step is to inject an intense blob of sodium vapour into the layer from a rocket, and to track its subsequent motion.

Fragments of water vapour

Water vapour soon gets broken up into fragments in the lower reaches of the upper atmosphere, under the bombardment of ultra-violet light: into atoms of hydrogen (H) and the fragment known as hydroxyl (OH). As the altitude is further increased, these hydroxyl fragments are destroyed in collisions with atomic oxygen $OH + O \longrightarrow H + O_2$. The molecular oxygen so formed is itself split up by photo-dissociation into atomic oxygen, the more readily the higher the altitude. The nett result of this aerial square dance is that above 60 miles water vapour is almost entirely replaced by atomic hydrogen and atomic oxygen. There is, however, an intermediate region in which there is a considerable concentration of hydroxyl fragments, which reveal themselves by emitting a very strong radiation in the infra-red, as we shall see.

Nitrogen

Paradoxically, less is known with certainty about nitrogen, the most abundant of the gases in the upper atmosphere, than about any other constituent. The nitrogen molecule does not split up directly into two atoms, as does the oxygen molecule, under irradiation by the ultra-violet light of the sun. Yet there are undoubtedly free nitrogen atoms in the upper atmosphere, and there is lively argument and speculation among scientists as to how they got there. There is evidence that their concentration falls off with increasing height, but it is also possible that the concentration of nitrogen in *any* form falls off relative to that of oxygen as the altitude increases. In short, the oxygen–nitrogen balance and the N_2–N balance in the upper atmosphere are both still unknown, and our ignorance on this point stands out as the most serious gap in our knowledge of the chemistry of the upper air. . . .

The night airglow

If our eyes could see in the infra-red, no night would ever be dark. . . .

The source of this infra-red radiation lies 50 or 60 miles above the earth. It comes from hydroxyl, formed in a state of electrical excitation in collisions between hydrogen atoms and ozone, which themselves are a legacy of the sun's day-time chemistry. This particular radiation, observable with special instruments, is quite remarkably intense. If it were emitted in the visible spectrum, it would make the night sky as bright as mid twilight.

Besides the infra-red radiation from hydroxyl, there are faint signals in the visible part of the spectrum, coming from sodium —already responsible for the twilight flash of yellow light—and also from atomic oxygen, again at a height of 50 or 60 miles, or even more. They are too faint to be seen with the naked eye, but are detectable with sufficiently sensitive optical instruments: the yellow light of excited sodium atoms, and two characteristic lines in the spectrum of atomic oxygen, one in the green and one in the red.

Together these four radiations—the yellow of sodium, the green and red of atomic oxygen, and the broad infra-red band of hydroxyl—make up the night airglow, the detailed study of which, particularly during the past decade, has set us a number of puzzles, the solution of which promises to be of great importance to our understanding of the upper atmosphere.

One of these puzzles is the radiation from atomic oxygen. When this radiation is studied in the laboratory, the emission of the green light is followed immediately by emission of the crimson red. Yet in the night airglow, while the green light increases in intensity during the evening hours, and fades with the approach of dawn, just the opposite occurs with the red radiation. What process, then, is going on up aloft which delays the emission of the red light for hours on end?

Then again, the night airglow, although it can be observed on any night of the year in all parts of the world, is not uniform, but patchy. This is particularly remarkable in the case of sodium, the light from which waxes and wanes with the seasons, in a way that leads us to conclude that the sodium layer winters near the Poles, and spends the summer above the tropics.

But if so, why?

Ions Electrons and Radio

The region of the upper atmosphere lying between 50 and 200 miles above the earth is known as the ionosphere. Here, as we have seen earlier in this chapter, photo-ionisation—the release of electrons from atoms and molecules under the bombardment of the more energetic light quanta—predominates over the less energetic process of photo-dissociation which we have so far been studying.

It is the presence of free electrons in the ionosphere that makes modern radio-communication possible. At least a thousand times lighter and more mobile than the positively charged ions, the free electrons are set swinging in unison with the radio-waves sent out from man-made radio-transmitters on land, in ships, or in aircraft, and so send back to earth the signals which would otherwise stream away into outer space. Over the whole arc of the sky they act together as a gigantic concave mirror, reflecting the up-coming radio-waves back to the earth-bound receivers.

Thus an intimate knowledge of the electrical nature of the ionosphere, leading to a better understanding of its capricious behaviour, is no subject for an ivory-tower study, but is of crucial importance to telecommunications generally—the world-wide transmission of script and speech, the reliability of the radio-navigation of ships and aircraft—not to mention the breathlessly urgent passage across the oceans, in news and picture, of the most up-to-the-minute movements of film-stars or television personalities.

Layers in the ionosphere

The concentration of free electrons in the ionosphere increases as the height above earth increases: not steadily, however, but in stages. . . .

Consider for a moment the mechanism of the release of free electrons by the irradiation of the upper atmosphere by short-wave radiation from the sun. Clearly, the number of electrons released from their parent atoms or molecules must increase as the number of atoms or molecules increases; that is, the concentration of free electrons for a specific solar radiation must become greater the lower the altitude. But acting against this trend is the always increasing absorption by these very same atoms or molecules of the energy of the solar radiation as it penetrates the atmosphere on its journey between sun and earth. So there must come a rise to a maximum, and then a falling off to zero, of the number of free electrons for which any one specific solar radiation is responsible.

There are at least two layers in the ionosphere responsible for the reflection, and so maintenance, of the waves of radio-communication: the so-called E-layer, or "Heaviside Layer", at an average height of 70 miles above earth; and the F-layer,

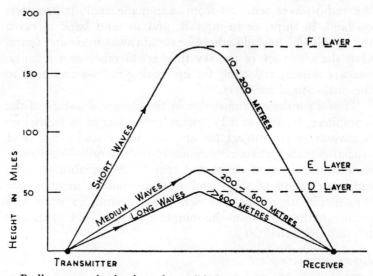

Radio-communication is made possible by the reflecting layers of the ionosphere.

or "Appleton Layer", lying around 150 miles high. What then are the kinds of solar radiation responsible for the creation of these two layers?

The answer to this question is even yet in some doubt. But we can today say this: that the creation of the F-layer comes most probably from the ionisation of atomic oxygen by the ultra-violet radiation from the sun, while the E-layer almost certainly comes from the more penetrating soft X-rays, originating in the outer regions of the solar atmosphere.

The concentration of free electrons in the F-layer is about

ten times as great as the concentration of free electrons in the E-layer. Now the higher the concentration of free electrons, the shorter the wave-length of the radio-waves reflected by them; so we find that the F-layer is responsible for the world-wide transmission of the short wave-band lying between 10 and 200 metres, and the E-layer for the transmission of the medium wave-band, 200 to 600 metres.

Below the E-layer lies still another ionised layer, the D-layer, which reflects the less frequently used long-wave band of between 600 and 3,000 metres or more. The D-layer also affects the transmission of the shorter radio-waves, since these must first penetrate it on their way to reflection at the higher-lying layers. Much of the sporadic disturbance of radio-communication in the most widely used wave-bands arises, in fact, from changes in the ionisation of the D-layer.

Night and day

Since the electron concentration in the ionosphere stems from short-wave radiations from the sun, it is not surprising that its electrical properties show a rhythmic variation as night follows day over the globe, with the concentration of electrons above any one meridian rising to a maximum at noon, and falling to a minimum at midnight. The effect of sunlight on the F-layer is particularly striking: during the day it splits into two layers, known as F_1 and F_2, which merge again into a single layer during the night hours.

One effect of sunlight on the E-layer is familiar to everyone interested in the reception of programmes from distant medium-wave broadcasting stations, which is notoriously better during the hours of darkness. This result, although it might appear at first sight to be paradoxical, is really quite simply explained. For by day the reflecting layer for the medium wave-band occurs at a level in the upper atmosphere where the air is sufficiently dense to damp out the oscillations of the free electrons which respond to the up-coming radio-waves, through collisions of the electrons with the surrounding molecules of air; while at night the medium wave-band is reflected at a higher level, where less energy is lost by the radio-wave to the air molecules, and so more is reflected back to earth.

If now we were to take an instantaneous picture of the whole canopy of the ionosphere, we should see its electrical character-istics as highly unsymmetrical, as between the sunlit hemisphere and the dark. What then are the effects on the ionosphere of the long polar nights and midnight suns of the polar regions, particularly of the practically unexplored continent of Ant-arctica? We have still to find the answer to that question.

Solar tides and the compass needle

The solar tides in our atmosphere, which as we have seen in Chapter 1 are probably accountable for the 24-hour day, are responsible for some interesting events in the ionosphere.

The whole atmosphere goes out and in like a concertina as the revolving earth carries it past the sun. In doing so, the electrically conducting layers of the ionosphere move across the

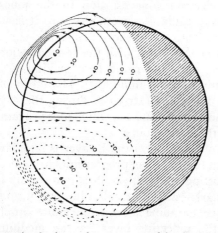

Dynamo currents in the ionosphere, measured in thousands of amperes, which result from the tidal motion of the earth's atmosphere.

lines of force of the earth's magnetic field. Electric currents are therefore induced in the ionosphere, in much the same way as they arise in the coil of a dynamo when it is set spinning be-tween the poles of its magnet. Flowing parallel to the earth's surface, predominantly in the E-layer, these dynamo currents, of many thousands of amperes, themselves set up a magnetic field, which affects all the compass needles in the sunlit hemisphere.

In thinking about the effect of the dynamo currents in the upper atmosphere on the compass needle, it is easier to imagine a fixed pattern of currents aloft, beneath which the earth rotates, rather than to try to picture their rise and decay above a given point on the earth's surface. The resulting current diagram is illustrated opposite.

Now imagine that we are in London Paris or New York, on an earth rotating below the current system of the northern hemisphere. In each case we should approach the overhead ring currents from the west, where their direction is towards the south: in the morning hours, therefore, our compass needle would be deflected from its mean position towards the east; in the afternoon hours, when we are leaving the daylight current system behind us, the overhead currents would be flowing south, and the magnetic needle would be deflected towards the west.

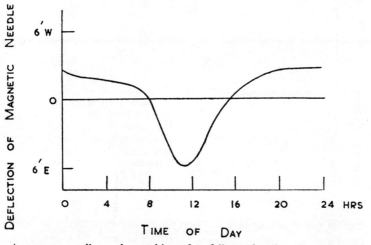

A compass needle on the earth's surface follows the changing pattern of the dynamo currents aloft.

How can we substantiate this picture of the sequence of the solar tides, the conducting ionosphere, the pattern of ionospheric dynamo currents, the daily variation of the magnetic declination? The answer is that we are already on the way. The first step was taken in 1951, when a rocket sent aloft from Huancoya in Peru, carrying a recording magnetic needle, sent word back to earth that the needle reversed its deflection in passing through the E-layer. In other words, the needle had passed beyond the level where it was deflected towards the right by a current flowing above it, to a level where it was deflected towards the left by a current flowing below it! But much still remains to be done before we can say that we have scanned in detail the complicated current system that the solar tides in the atmosphere produce in the E-layer.

The F_2-layer and the winds of summer

We should expect to find seasonal variations in the electron concentration of the ionosphere; namely, an increase in the daylight concentration in the summer months over that of winter. This is indeed what we find in the D-layer and the E-layer;

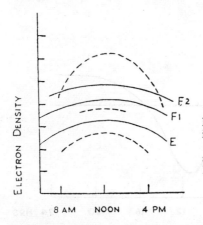

Seasonal variations in the ionised layers. The electron density is higher in summer (full line) than in winter (broken line) for both the E-layer and the F_1-layer, but for the F_2-layer the curves are reversed.

but in the F_2-layer just the reverse of the expected happens—the electron concentration is *higher* in winter than in summer.

This seemingly paradoxical behaviour has only recently found an explanation. The F_2-layer, lying at the boundary of our atmosphere, is heated directly by the sun, to a temperature of perhaps 1,000° centigrade. When we remember that

water boils at 100° centigrade, we realise at once that the
F₂-layer is extremely hot. It was thought at first that a simple
expansion of the F_2-layer under the summer sun, diminishing
the density of ionisation, might account for its anomalous behaviour; but more careful calculation showed that the effect of
expansion, although undoubtedly it exists, was insufficient to
account for the observed diminution of electron concentration
at midsummer.

The full explanation lies in the fact that the world-wide heating and cooling of the F_2-layer as the sun rises and sets must
give rise to violent horizontal winds in this region of the upper
atmosphere. These winds must carry with them the free
electrons (and ions) which are abundantly present in the F-
layers. These electrically charged particles resist being jostled
across the lines of force of the earth's magnetic field, but will
move quite freely in spirals along their length. Now the magnetic lines of force over most parts of the earth are inclined to
the horizontal, so the effect of a horizontal wind will be to drive
the ions and electrons upwards and downwards before it. The
result is a decrease in electron density in the region in which the
wind is blowing; and moreover, since the heating and cooling
which produces the wind is more extreme in summer than in
winter, we should expect to find that the electron density in the
F_2-layer is lower in summer than in winter, as is indeed the case.

The F_2-layer, which makes long-distance radio-communication in the short wave-band possible, is technically by far the most
important region of the ionosphere. Thus a detailed study of the
ionospheric winds becomes a matter of great practical importance. Some of the methods which are being employed in the
investigation are reviewed later, in Chapter 7.

"Sporadic E"

Mention has already been made of sporadic disturbances in
radio-communication due to variations in the ionisation of the
D-layer. There is, however, another type of sudden disturbance, affecting the short wave-band lying between 10 and
20 metres. Normally, radio-waves of this length are reflected by
the high-lying F-layer, in virtue of its high concentration of

free electrons; but quite unpredictably these waves may be reflected from a much lower level, located in the E-layer, sometimes momentarily, sometimes for as much as an hour or more. When we remember that radio-transmitters in the short waveband all use beamed transmission from one point to another on the earth's surface, this unpredictable behaviour of the E-layer is seen to be a serious matter. Yet "sporadic E" remains the outstanding riddle of the ionosphere.

One of the more promising lines of attack has been the study of the death of meteors as they come into our atmosphere from outer space. As these fragments of broken comets and planets dive earthwards, they are made white hot by the friction of the air they are passing through, and finally disintegrate completely, as "shooting stars".

Nowadays, meteors can be observed both night and day by the reflection of radar-waves, or better pulses, from the trail of ionised air they leave behind them, rather like the vapour trail of a jet aircraft. There is no doubt that the great crematorium of the meteors is the E-layer, so it was natural to ask whether there was any connection between the frequency of occurrence of sporadic E, and the meteor showers which recur quite regularly at certain seasons of the year. At one time it seemed that there was such a connection; in fact a strong meteor shower may raise the ionisation in the E-layer to a point where reflection of the short waves can indeed occur in it. Unfortunately, however, there is ample evidence that sporadic E can appear when there are no meteors about at all!

Once again we find ourselves on the boundary of present knowledge.

Whistlers

Every radio ham worth his salt has at one time or another listened to "whistlers"—those long-drawn-out, descending wails that can so often be heard on audio-frequency. Whistlers are indeed the easiest possible radio phenomenon for the amateur to observe: to hear them he needs only an aerial, and an audio-frequency amplifier such as is built in to any gramophone. But the discovery of the real origin and behaviour of whistlers only came in the last few years, and this new knowledge is likely to be of very great importance in a study of the ultimate reaches of the earth's atmosphere.

It is now quite certain that the origin of every whistler is a lightning-flash somewhere on the globe. The crack of the flash can of course also be heard on audio-frequency, and if the lightning has struck anywhere within 500 miles of the receiver, then *invariably* it is followed by at least one whistler, sometimes by as many as five or six, each more long drawn out and fainter than the last. How, then, does a single lightning flash father a whole family of whistlers?

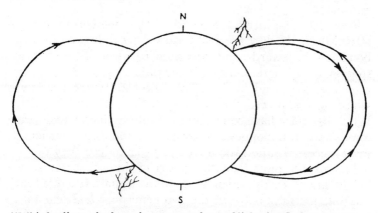

"Whistlers" are the long-drawn-out echoes of lightning flashes, bouncing backwards and forwards between the two hemispheres.

The explanation seems at first sight quite fantastic, but it fits the facts in every detail, as we shall see. It is this: that the lightning flash produces a radio signal, which follows a line of force of the earth's magnetic field to its termination on the ground in the opposite hemisphere, and is then bounced back to its point of origin!

Now for the details. The radio signal from the sharp crack of the lightning flash is of course not on one wave-length only: it is a radio *noise* on all sorts of wave-lengths at once. As the sharp radio pulse travels upwards through the ionosphere, the shorter waves travel faster than the longer ones; and because they are electro-magnetic waves, they all, short and long alike, travel fastest along a line of magnetic force near the vertical at the place they came from: that is, the point where the flash first struck.

The farther the waves travel, the more they get spread out, and so from the length of the first whistler heard in an audio-receiver in, say, London, following the crack of the parent flash, the distance the waves have travelled can be calculated. This distance comes out at the enormous figure of 15,000 miles, which is just the length of a double journey along a line of force of the earth's magnetic field, from London to the Antipodes and back.

Next take the increasing length of the members of a family of whistlers. If they are really caused by a drawn-out signal bouncing backwards and forwards between the two hemi-spheres, their lengths must be in the ratio 2 : 4 : 6 : 8—as indeed they are. ... And finally comes the case where a family of whistlers is *not* preceded by a sharp click in the audio-receiver. Why, they must have come from a lightning flash which struck somewhere in the opposite hemisphere; and if so, their lengths must increase in the ratio 1 : 3 : 5 : 7—as indeed they do.

Perhaps the most astonishing part of the whole story is the height above earth which these audio-signals reach in their multiple journeys between the two hemispheres. It cannot be less than 7,000 miles, which is several times the estimated height of the exosphere, the spray zone at the boundary of the earth's atmosphere. Clearly, the intensive study of whistlers is going to be of great importance in opening up the scientific explora-tion of a new territory on the edge of space.

The ionosphere and the sun cycle

Measurements of the total amount of the sun's light and heat reaching the astronomers' instruments on earth, made with the greatest care over many years, had shown it to be so steady that it received the name of "the solar constant". It remained steady, moreover, during the periods of enhanced eruptive activity on the sun, which have long been known to recur at approximately 11-year intervals.

Hence it was a complete surprise to the astronomers when the radio-scientists discovered that in its output of light in the far ultra-violet, unobservable at the earth's surface, the sun is a *variable star*. For if the yearly average of the electron density in the ionosphere at noon is plotted against time over a period of years, it is found to follow the 11-year cycle of solar activity!

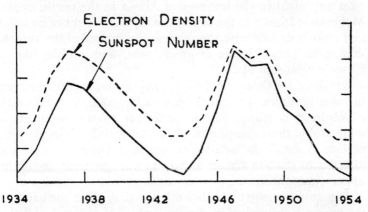

The electron density in the ionosphere waxes and wanes in step with the 11-year sunspot cycle.

This can mean only one thing: that the sun's output of ultra-violet light, which gives birth to the free electrons in the ionosphere, waxes and wanes in step with the increase and decrease in the number of sunspots, which likewise follows an 11-year cycle. Are the sunspots themselves responsible for the enhanced emission of ultra-violet light from the sun's disc? Or is its source the solar flares which so often accompany the spots? The answer to these questions must await an examination of the evidence which has been vigorously sought within the last two decades, by solar observatories all over the world, such as we shall make in the next chapter.

The aurora

On the evening of January 25, 1938, a BBC evening news bulletin alerted its listeners to watch the northern sky for an especially brilliant display of the aurora borealis. Many thousands of people saw the aurora that cloudless night for the first time in their lives. Many of these same people may see another such display in 1957.

Normally the displays are staged, the aurora borealis in the north, the aurora australis in the south, in two great amphitheatres around the North and South Magnetic Poles. On almost any night in the latitudes of Alaska in the north, or the McQuarrie Islands in the south, the sky at a height of 60 miles and more is draped with the shimmering curtain of the aurora, shining in pastel shades of green, rose, and purple, like a gigantic neon sign aloft.

But there are times when displays of the aurora are observed in lower latitudes, the aurora borealis for example as far south as Naples or Bombay. And when the records are examined, it is found that these exceptional displays invariably coincide with periods of maximum activity on the sun. Once again we are directed to the sun for an answer to our questions about the upper atmosphere. . . .

The answer we get is sufficiently startling: that the cause of the aurora is the arrival in our atmosphere of material particles shot out from the erupting sun. These particles, electrified fragments of atomic hydrogen, are channelled towards the Poles along the lines of force of the earth's magnetic field, until they are moving fast enough, and in sufficient numbers, to excite the molecules of the rarefied upper air to emit their characteristic luminous spectra.

The great auroral displays are accompanied by violent magnetic storms in the ionosphere, when radio-communication over the whole earth can be seriously disrupted for days on end, and even compass navigation may be affected. These great magnetic storms can also be traced to the arrival in the earth's magnetic field of the same corpuscles from the sun as give rise to the aurora. . . .

It is time we looked more closely at the sun.

CHAPTER 5

SUNSPOTS AND SOLAR FLARES

The birth of a sunspot

VIEWED through a solar telescope, the whole of the sun's bright disc is seen to be studded with a pattern of roughly circular granules, each one of which may measure as much as 1,000 miles across its diameter. The granules wax and wane in brightness as we watch them, flashing out and subsiding again within a minute or so, conveying a vivid impression of the boiling and seething of the incandescent ball of the gaseous sun.

Every so often the granules in a particular area of the sun's disc separate, and between them appears a small dark area, or *pore*. Sometimes the dark pores simply disappear, but again several of them may coalesce to form a new-born sunspot, which may grow until it covers an area on the sun's surface of over 5,000 million square miles.

More than 60 per cent of all the sunspots that appear on the sun's disc occur in pairs. As a newly born pair moves westward on the rotating sun, the two separate, as if repelling each other, until they are perhaps 10,000 miles apart. All this time they are growing in size, the leading spot more diffuse in outline. They reach full size usually in about a week or ten days, and may have a life of as long as several months. But eventually they dwindle and disappear, the following spot on the average four times as fast as the leader.

The sunspot cycle

The number of sunspots observable in any one year waxes and wanes over an approximately 11-year period, which may, however, be as short as 8 years or as long as 13 years. The last maximum occurred in 1947 and the last minimum in 1954. The next maximum is therefore due in 1957. The number of sunspots recorded at the 1947 maximum was the highest for over a century; and judging from the rapid build-up towards the 1957 maximum, which has been recorded in 1955–56, it too promises to be something of a record.

The appearance of sunspots on the sun's disc is confined to a broad band about the sun's equator, lying between solar latitudes 35° north and 35° south. At the beginning of a cycle, the first spots occur at the boundaries of the equatorial zone; as the cycle advances, the spots appear in ever-increasing numbers, always closer to the equator, until at sunspot maximum they are concentrated in a narrow belt 10° north and south of the equator itself. Then their numbers in this narrow zone die away, while the first spots of the succeeding cycle begin to appear, in small numbers, in the higher solar latitudes.

All these phenomena are elegantly displayed in the celebrated Greenwich "Butterfly Diagram".

Magnetic fields of sunspots

Sunspots appear as dark areas on the sun's disc. But they are not as black as they are painted: their darkness is merely an effect of contrast. Actually, they emit an extremely bright spectrum, but at a temperature more than 1000° below that of their surroundings. What, then, is the cooling mechanism which is responsible for this state of affairs? The answer is a strange one—the spots are magnetised!

When a gas is excited to emit light between the poles of a powerful electro-magnet, the characteristic lines in its spectrum are split up into two or more separate components. So also are the lines in the spectrum of a sunspot, when the light coming from it is analysed in the astronomers' spectrographs.

Now the separation between the components of a spectral line split in a magnetic field is a measure of the strength of the field: and so we find that the magnetic fields associated with sunspots are as strong as can be maintained in a terrestrial laboratory between the poles of a magnet which are perhaps a few feet apart. On the sun, however, these fields are maintained over distances amounting to tens of thousands of miles.

A closer examination of the spectra of sunspots tells us that the ionised gases of the sun's interior, streaming upwards from

the bottom of the 5,000-mile-deep sunspot crater, are guided
by the lines of force of its magnetic field, fanning out when they
reach the lip of the crater at a speed of perhaps 4,000 miles
an hour. It is this rapid escape and dispersal of the gases in the
magnetic field of the sunspot, acting against the pull of the
sun's gravitational force, that cools them so far below the average temperature of the sun's disc.

Magnetic polarity of sunspots

When the components of a spectral line which has been split
in a magnetic field are closely examined, the light from them
is found to be polarised, in much the same way as sunlight that
has passed through a pair of polaroid sun-glasses. Careful
analysis of this polarised light can tell us the direction of the
magnetic lines of force relative to that of the light beam reaching our instruments.

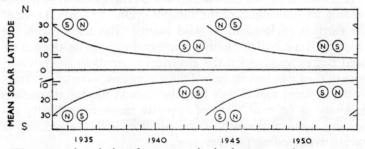

The magnetic polarity of sunspot pairs is always opposite on opposite
sides of the sun's equator, and reverses at the commencement of each new
cycle.

In this way it has been found that the sunspots of a typical
pair are always of opposite magnetic polarity—if one is a north-
pole, the other is a south-pole. Moreover, in any one 11-year
cycle the leading spot in the group north of the sun's equator
is always of the same sign, while south of the equator the polarities are the other way round. In the next cycle the polarities
north and south of the equator are reversed. From this point
of view, therefore, we should speak of a 22-year rather than an
11-year cycle, even though there seems to be no observable

difference in the effects on terrestrial phenomena as between one "half-cycle" and the other.

The sun's magnetism

At this juncture one would like to be able to present a reasoned explanation of the sunspot cycle. One would like to trace the sequence of events through the years so that the birth of the sunspots north and south of the sun's equator, carrying magnetic fields of opposite polarity; their drift towards the equator; their reversal of magnetic sign as the next group waxes with the waning of the last—would all fall into place in a clean-cut theoretical blue-print.

But here we can only guess. All the same, we are irresistibly reminded of the theories of the earth's magnetism, which we have found earlier on to be almost certainly connected with a turbulent motion of the earth's liquid core.

It is indeed in this direction that current speculation is proceeding on the subject of the sunspot cycle. The liquid core of the earth is enclosed in its solid mantle. But not so with the sun, which is a ball of highly compressed gas. So on the sun we need not be surprised if the electrical currents in the interior, born of the turbulent motion of the sun's gases, were to penetrate to the surface; and if they did, they would display themselves precisely as pairs of areas of opposite magnetic polarity, appearing north and south of the equator, with the polarity of each corresponding pair reversed.

But why an 11-year cycle of drift towards the equator, and of the recurrence of the same magnetic polarities every 22 years? Nobody knows.

Prominences

The escape of the internal magnetic field of the sun is evidenced, not only in the more familiar sunspots, but also in the solar prominences, to be seen riding out thousands of miles above the sun's disc at times of solar eclipse.

The prominences very often show arch-like forms, rising into the sun's outer atmosphere—the solar corona—and falling back towards the sharply defined disc of the sun. But they don't rise and fall as if under gravity, but far more as if they were guided upwards and downwards along the curving lines of magnetic force of a magnetised sphere.

Now the prominences are visible only because they are cooler than the surrounding gases, and hence show up by contrast against the white light of the surrounding corona. Hence we are more than tempted to ascribe their appearance to the guidance of the rather more highly condensed gases along the lines of magnetic force of the sun's general magnetic field.

The prominence cycle

The frequency of appearance of the prominences, and the solar latitudes in which they appear, follow the sunspot cycle. There are, however, two distinct sets of prominences, one set appearing in the sunspot belt, the other in more northerly and southerly solar latitudes.

In the first set, which is the more important, prominences begin to appear in small numbers at the edges of the sunspot belt within a year or two after the minimum of the sunspot cycle. Then they increase in number and size with the spots, and follow them with a lag of about 10° in latitude in their drift towards the solar equator. Like the spots, they die away again in number towards the next minimum.

The second set begins to appear around solar latitudes 45° north and south at about the time of sunspot minimum, whence they drift towards the poles, attaining their maximum numbers some two years after sunspot maximum.

The prominences are on the whole considerably more stable than the spots, and may be followed through as many as five periods of revolution of the sun. This feature of the prominences may be connected with phenomena in the earth's atmosphere, such as the aurorae, which tend to follow a 27-day cycle in rhythm with the rotation of the sun.

Flares

Quite unpredictably, the sun's atmosphere above a sunspot, over an area of perhaps 1,000 million square miles, may within a few minutes erupt into intense activity, blazing out with a light ten times as brilliant as its surroundings, which then dies away again within the hour.

These explosive events in the sun are known as solar flares. They always occur above sunspots, although not all sunspots give rise to flares. They are associated more frequently with spot pairs than with single spots. A flare-active pair may give rise to as many as thirty or forty flares in a single passage across the sun's disc.

The flares not only emit light, they spew out vast quantities of gaseous matter into space. When photographed at the edge of the sun's disc, the flare prominences completely dwarf the normal solar prominences in size and violence, rising to a height of half a million miles at a speed of 500 miles a second. Some of the gas so ejected is seen to return to the sun, but much of it is shot away into space for good.

The appearance of a flare on the sun is invariably followed by a complicated series of events in the earth's upper atmosphere, some of which we have hinted at in the last chapter. It is in fact the solar flares, and *not* the sunspots which produce them, that affect us on the earth; and this fascinating new knowledge we can now follow out in some detail.

Terrestrial effects of solar flares

The terrestrial effects of solar flares are of two kinds, instantaneous and delayed. The instantaneous effects accompany the appearance of *any* flare on the sun's disc, and are confined to the sunlit hemisphere of the earth. The delayed effects occur roughly one day after the appearance of a flare which is situated near the central meridian of the sun's disc, not from any flare at all. The delayed effects are worldwide.

The instantaneous effects are all traceable to a sudden increase in the ionisation of the upper atmosphere, following the arrival of ultra-violet light from the flare. The delayed effects are due to the arrival of material particles shot out from the flare.

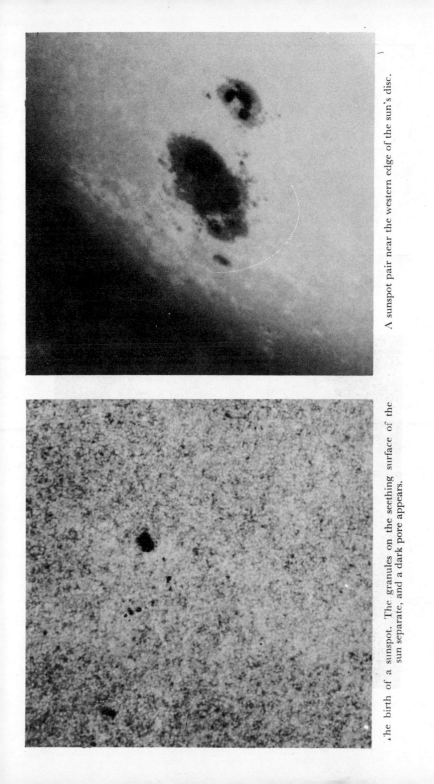

A sunspot pair near the western edge of the sun's disc.

The birth of a sunspot. The granules on the seething surface of the sun separate, and a dark pore appears.

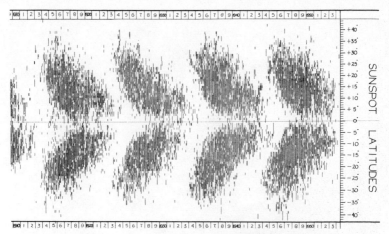

The Greenwich "butterfly diagram", showing how the sunspots wax and wane in number as they advance and retire to and from the sun's equator.

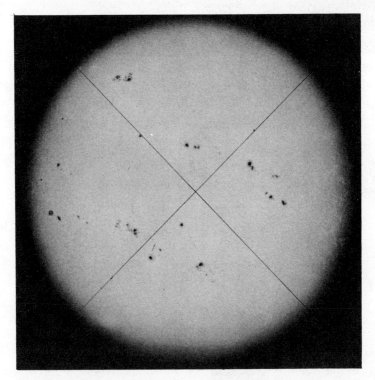

Sunspots at the approach of the last maximum of 1947, lying in two well defined zones on either side of the sun's equator.

Instantaneous effects

We shall deal here with three effects which occur simultaneously with the observation of a flare situated *anywhere* on the sun's disc—namely, effects on the compass needle, radio-fade-outs, and the sudden enhancement of atmospherics.

Magnetic crochets

At the same instant as an intense flare is observed on the sun by the astronomers in their telescopes, heralding the arrival at the earth of the light given out by the flare, the magnetic needle in every geomagnetic laboratory in the sunlit hemisphere gives a sudden kick, technically known as a "crochet", from its appearance on the magnetic records.

Now we already know that the to-and-fro variation of a compass needle throughout a normal day is traceable to the dynamo currents which flow in the E-layer as the result of solar tides in the atmosphere. We should immediately suspect, therefore, that the kick of the magnetic needle which accompanies a solar flare is caused by a sudden increase in the dynamo currents, such as would immediately follow an instantaneous increase in the ionisation of the E-layer by the intense ultra-violet radiation from the flare.

Up to a point, this explanation is strongly supported by a closer analysis of the direction and magnitude of the kicks. For an enhancement of the dynamo currents should lead always to an increase in the deflection of the compass needle, at the instant of the flare, in the same direction as it is already tending at any one particular place at any one time. And this is exactly what the analysis shows.

There is one difficulty, however. Crochets are observed only when the flare is sufficiently intense to cause strong ionisation in the D-layer. This may mean one of two things: either that the soft X-rays which are supposed to account for the normal ionisation of the E-layer are produced only by the more intense flares; or that the "crochet currents" are fleeting currents in the D-layer itself. It may be that the final answer must await the launching of a rocket carrying a recording magnetic needle, at the same instant in which flare and crochet are observed.

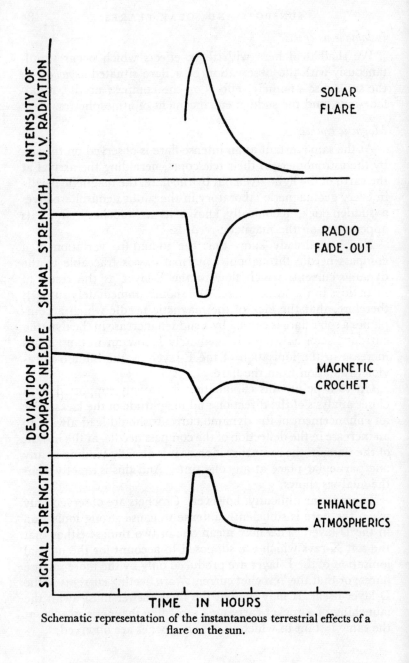

Schematic representation of the instantaneous terrestrial effects of a flare on the sun.

Radio fade-outs

Sudden fade-outs in short-wave radio transmissions occur simultaneously with the appearance of solar flares. The cause of fade-outs is quite certainly the enhancement of ionisation in the low-lying D-layer, as a result of its irradiation by the intense ultra-violet light from the flare.

Normally, the short-wave radio signals easily penetrate the D-layer, to be reflected by the more highly ionised layers above, in particular the F-layer. At first sight one might expect that they would be *reflected* at the D-layer, when its electron concentration suddenly rises. In actual fact, however, they are *absorbed* in the D-layer, because the density of the gases at this lower level of the ionosphere is great enough to steal the energy of oscillation away from the free electrons, which alone are sufficiently mobile to transmit and reflect the up-coming radio-waves. The result, then, is the fade-out of the short-wave transmissions which is observed in practice.

Just as with the effects of a solar flare on the deviation of the compass needle, so the radio fade-outs are observed only in the sunlit hemisphere. Night-time transmissions are unaffected. Thus if a flare is observed in London in the early morning, radio communication on short wave-lengths with India or Japan is most seriously disturbed. If the flare is seen at the London observatories in the afternoon, short-wave transmissions to the Americas are interrupted.

Atmospherics

Still another effect of solar flares is an abrupt enhancement of atmospherics on long wave-lengths, arising from the sudden increase in electron density in the D-layer, which makes the layer temporarily a much more efficient reflector of long radio-waves. Nowadays comparatively few radio transmitters work on the long wave-lengths which are reflected by the D-layer, so that this enhancement of the long-wave atmospherics must be classed as a subsidiary effect as far as interference with everyday radio transmission is concerned. Nevertheless, astronomers now make ingenious use of these long-wave atmospherics as a means of recording solar flares which, through cloudy weather perhaps, might otherwise escape observation. They have built special receivers which add up the crackles caused by the lightning flashes of tropical thunderstorms—the chief cause of long-wave atmospherics—and record the total of the addition sum as a line traced out by a pen on a moving strip of paper. . . . Then comes a solar flare: and although of course the number of lightning flashes is not influenced thereby in the least, the signals received from them after reflection at the D-layer are instantly increased, and the pen of the recorder makes a big addition sum. A neat case of poacher turned gamekeeper!

Delayed effects

We now turn to the delayed effects on earth of flares on the sun—magnetic storms lasting for several days, spectacular displays of the aurora—which occur about a day after the appearance of a flare on or near the meridian line of the sun.

We have stated earlier, quite baldly, that these delayed effects are due to the arrival in the earth's atmosphere of material particles from the sun. What evidence is there for this remarkable statement?

Corpuscles from the sun

The magnetic storms in the ionosphere, affecting radio-communication for days instead of several minutes, as with the transient radio fade-outs, occur not simultaneously, but on an average 26 hours *after* the appearance of certain particular flares. This single fact alone points to a material origin of the storms, for light takes only 8 minutes to get from sun to earth.

But there is the fact that solar flares, no matter how intense, that occur far out towards the periphery of the sun's disc, are *not* followed by magnetic storms in the earth's upper atmosphere; whereas there is a practically one-to-one coincidence between the number of flares near the centre of the sun's disc and that of great magnetic storms on earth. This points straight to the ejection of particles at right angles to the sun's surface, in contradistinction to the all-round emission of light.

Then comes the direct evidence of the ejection of particles of hydrogen from the flares themselves. Atomic hydrogen, as is well known, consists of positive protons and negative electrons, which emit the characteristic carnation-red light of atomic hydrogen when the separated particles reunite. This red light is typical of the visible spectrum of the solar flares—but with a difference. The red light which signals the final capture of an electron by a proton to form atomic hydrogen is strongly displaced towards the blue in the light from a solar flare. This corresponds in the range of audible sound to the rise in pitch of the whistle of a railway engine as the express comes towards us, standing on a wayside platform: in other words, the hydrogen emitted by the flare is coming straight at us.

Finally, the same carnation-red hydrogen line has been observed in the spectrum of the aurora which accompanies the magnetic storms in the ionosphere. And again the line is displaced towards the blue: showing that the hydrogen particles are coming down out of the sky at a speed of 3,000 miles a second.

All in all, therefore, it is not too much to say that the evidence is strong that the great magnetic storms arise from the arrival in the earth's atmosphere of hydrogen particles shot out in the eruption above its sunspot of a solar flare.

The genesis of a magnetic storm

What, then, is the sequence of events between the outburst of a solar flare near the centre of the sun's disc and the onset of a magnetic storm in the ionosphere? The answer to this question is still a matter of dispute, but a conjecture which is probably not far from the truth traces the successive stages of the onset of a great magnetic storm somewhat as follows.

First, there is the ejection of charged particles of hydrogen— protons and electrons—from the flare itself. The majority of these we don't see at all, only those which recombine to give the hydrogen spectrum as they leave the flare. But there must be both protons and electrons in about equal numbers coming away from the flare; for otherwise, particles of only one sign would repel each other in space and never reach the earth at all.

From the amount by which the pitch of the hydrogen lines is

increased, we can calculate that the protons and electrons must
finally leave the sun with a speed of around 1,000 miles a
second, in agreement with the time of approximately 26 hours
which they take to traverse the 93 million miles between sun
and earth. . . .

But now this blast from the sun's shot-gun approaches the
earth, and sweeps into the earth's magnetic field. There will

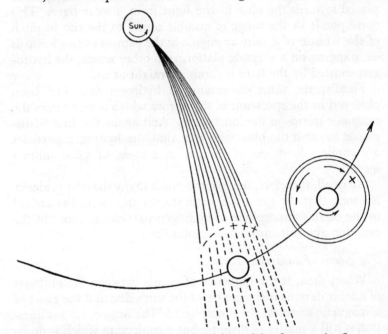

How the earth traps the charged particles arriving from a solar flare,
after a day's journey from the sun, in a ring high above the equator.

then be an immediate reaction between the earth's magnetic
field and the conducting face of the advancing stream: first,
there will be a general retardation of the speed of the approaching particles, which produces a hollow in the stream, in which
the earth is finally trapped; second, there will be a separation
of the protons and electrons in the face of the stream, such that
the protons move clockwise, the electrons counter-clockwise.
Thus the protons are guided *against* the direction of rotation of

the earth, the electrons *with* its rotation. Relative to the earth, therefore, the protons move faster than the electrons; so that finally, when the earth is completely trapped by the sun-born particles, and the blast has passed on, there is a ring current of many hundreds of thousands of amperes flowing clockwise high above the earth around the Equator, whose attendant magnetic field is opposed to that of the earth.

Characteristics of magnetic storms

The facts about great magnetic storms are these: The storm is heralded by a sudden very temporary increase in the general magnetic field of the earth. This is followed by a decrease in the field, which lasts for several days. The storm is world-wide, occurring over sunlit and dark hemispheres alike.

All these facts are elegantly accounted for by the hypothetical sun-born equatorial ring current. The initial increase in the earth's field is accounted for by the back reaction of the hollow in the advancing corpuscular stream, which temporarily compresses the lines of magnetic force around the earth, so increasing the field; the subsequent weakening of the field is accounted for by the clockwise sense of the ring current; the decay of the storm is accounted for by the gradual leakage of the ring current, consequent on the repulsion of particles of the same charge. And of course the storm is world-wide, since the ring current encircles the earth.

Displays of the aurora

The displays of the aurora which accompany and follow the great magnetic storms are also explainable as a consequence of the trapping by the earth of hydrogen particles ejected from solar flares: protons and electrons circling in a gigantic ring current high above the Equator.

Particles which leave the ring under the electrical repulsion of those of the same charge can do so only along the lines of force of the earth's magnetic field. Channelled polewards along the lines of force, they gain speed all the while, to come hurtling downwards towards the earth in the northern and southern auroral zones.

The characteristic colours of the auroral displays, when analysed spectroscopically, show quite unmistakably that they are
produced by atoms and molecules of the upper atmosphere
which have been excited to emit light under the bombardment
of swift-moving protons and electrons. It is significant that
bombardment by *both* these constituents of atomic hydrogen
must be called in to account for the spectra observed, both in
the aurora itself, and under controlled conditions in laboratory
discharge tubes.

The areas on the earth's surface from which auroral displays
aloft are observed, wax and wane with the 11-year solar cycle.
At times of maximum solar activity, displays of the aurora
borealis have been observed as far south as the Equator. This
latitude shift could arise in two ways: either from an actual
expansion of the auroral zone, or from a greater height above
earth of the aurora itself. Both would follow as a natural consequence of the bombardment of the upper atmosphere by protons and electrons flying out from the equatorial ring current.

Displays in the lower latitudes are predominantly red in
colour, a sure indication of an aurora at very high level, where
the atoms of atomic oxygen responsible for the crimson-red
light are most abundant. The lower portions of the display,
shining with the violet and blue of molecular nitrogen, are below
the horizon for the lower latitudes.

All we have said above is based on observations in the
northern hemisphere. To date the aurora australis has been
but scantily observed. Thus we don't even know whether displays in the northern and southern hemispheres occur simultaneously, as one would expect if the equatorial ring current is
the source of the bombarding particles... An intensive study of
the aurora australis from observational stations on the Antarctic
continent is urgently called for.

Small magnetic storms

The so-called "great magnetic storms" so far discussed are
characterised by their sudden onset and their short duration.
Their source is quite certainly the solar flares associated with
sunspots.

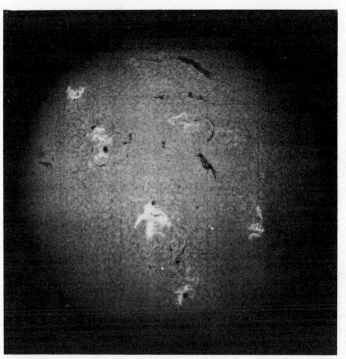

Flares on the sun. The picture also shows many sunspots and several prominences, which appear dark when photographed against the sun's background.

A giant prominence on the sun, arched as if the flaming gases in the chromosphere were guided by a magnetic field.

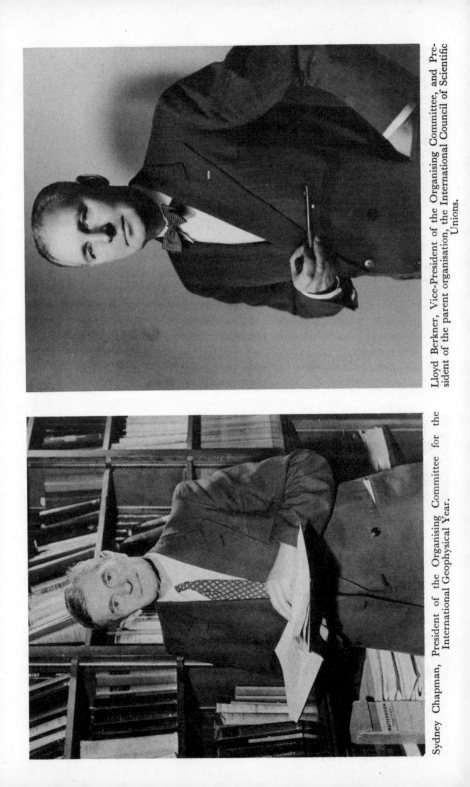

Sydney Chapman, President of the Organising Committee for the International Geophysical Year.

Lloyd Berkner, Vice-President of the Organising Committee, and President of the parent organisation, the International Council of Scientific Unions.

But there is another class of magnetic storm—the "small" magnetic storm—whose origin on the sun is still a mystery. The small magnetic storms are much less intense than the great storms associated with the solar flares; their onset in the earth's upper atmosphere is gradual rather than sudden; and, most indicative of all, they tend to *recur* after an interval of about 27 days.

Now the period of rotation of the sun is one of 27 days. There can therefore be little doubt that the small magnetic storms are to be traced eventually to some disturbance on the sun, more long-lived than the abrupt and violent flares, which presents itself to the earth at least once, and sometimes more than once, as the sun rotates about its axis.

The terrestrial effects of the small magnetic storms are so similar, if on a reduced scale, to those of the great storms, that the consensus of opinion is that they too must come from a bombardment of the earth by charged particles of hydrogen from the sun. But the source of these particles is still in doubt: although there are indications that they may come from the coronal prominences, which can be recognised as reappearing after a revolution of the sun has brought them into sight once more. . . .

Here once again we find ourselves on the boundary of modern knowledge.

PART II

TOWARDS NEW HORIZONS

CHAPTER 6

A YEAR OF PLANNED OBSERVATION

ON July 1 1957 scientists of fifty-four countries begin a concerted attack on the problems of man's physical environment, seeking answers to more than some of the open questions which still bar the way to its proper understanding. At least 5,000 men and women are being directly recruited to staff the hundreds of stations which have been set up for the simultaneous world-wide observation of the winds aloft, of the earth's magnetic field, of the aurora borealis and aurora australis, of the dance of the electrified particles in the upper atmosphere, of the impact of the cosmic rays on the earth's canopy of air, and of the face of the sun. The stations will be manned until the close of the year 1958, at a total cost to all the participating countries of at least £100 million.

First steps

No great enterprise such as this ever took shape of itself. There must first come the idea, springing to life in the mind of a man. The idea of an International Geophysical Year came to Lloyd Berkner back in the spring of 1950, during an evening of informal talk among fellow scientists in the Maryland home of James van Allen. Among the company was Sydney Chapman, and these two men sparked the beginnings of an undertaking that has surprised them. . . . And there you have the second criterion for the launching of a great endeavour: that no matter how brilliant the idea, unless it comes in over the threshold of the already latent wishes in the minds of many, you may as well write it off. That was emphatically *not* the case with the idea of a world-wide attack on the problems of man's own environment. Too many people were aware that hitherto observations had been made haphazard, with instruments which had not been standardised one with another, the results written up in a

97

form which made comparison with similar observations unduly difficult.

The protagonists

Sydney Chapman and Lloyd Berkner complement each other perfectly. Chapman is the academic, integrating brain. Berkner is the man of scientific affairs, the sort of man who goes into a committee meeting having made up everybody's mind for him beforehand.

Chapman comes of Lancashire Quaker stock, and doubtless his zeal for international collaboration has its origins in that very fact. Nevertheless he has never sought greatness in the counsels of international scientific endeavour. He has had it thrust upon him, as the dubious reward of his gigantic contributions to the earth sciences. Throughout a long working life— he is now 68—he has devoted his outstanding talents, with complete singleness of purpose, to the advancement of the academic understanding of the behaviour of gases, of geomagnetism, of the ionosphere, of solar and terrestrial relationships, until today he speaks magistrally on an astounding number of geophysical topics. . . . Swimming and cycling have kept him remarkably fit, and he walks today with the gait of a young man.

Berkner is a man of action. . . . He was radio-officer with the expedition of Admiral Byrd to the Antarctic in 1928–30. He was a key man in "selling" radar to the United States Navy in the last war, and characteristically did so, not only from shore, but on the ships in actual battle in the Pacific. Nevertheless, he has made important contributions to radio-science and to our knowledge of the workings of the ionosphere. At the age of 52, he is President of Associated Universities Incorporated, a joint venture of a number of the leading universities of the United States, which is crystallised in the Laboratories of Brookhaven in New York State, and in the nascent radio-astronomical station in Virginia: where apparatus for the production of ultra high-speed particles on the one hand, or radio-telescopes for the observation of the cosmos on the other, are installed for the benefit of all the participants.

Ways and means

These two men, then, talking in the spring of 1950 in the house of a mutual friend, put the following questions to themselves: How can this enterprise of a world-wide attack on the physical problems of our environment best be achieved? How can the scientists of the world, the people who will have to *do* the job, be most directly reached? Who should make the first outline of the programme, and who should execute it? When should the attack begin?

Both were agreed at once on the timing of the programme: 1957–58 would be the next period of maximum activity on the sun, when the terrestrial effects of sunspots and solar flares would come to another peak.... And both were agreed that the vessel which should carry the flag of the effort should be the International Council of Scientific Unions.

ICSU

We are all legitimately weary of international alphabetology. I have in fact a private joke of my own—an imaginary organisation called UTCAA, which might well signify some such a title as Universal Trust for the Conservation of Ancient Archives, but which really stands for Uncle Tom Cobley and All!

But ICSU (rhymes with "Fix You"), which I am proud to serve, is another story. It is a unique organisation. Unlike the numerous organs of the United Nations—UNESCO, FAO, WHO, and so forth—it is not controlled by the governments of a set of member states. It is a free association of two kinds of scientific bodies: the International Scientific Unions, and the learned Academies of forty nations.

Therein lies its strength, in spite of the fact that its own proper funds, contributed by its national and scientific members, amount to no more than some £10,000 a year. For the International Unions—of Astronomy, of Geophysics, of Radio-Science—can propose; and the forty nations, through their National Academies—the Royal Society of London, the National Academy of Washington, the Académie des Sciences de Paris, the Academy of Sciences of Moscow—can dispose.

Let us look for a moment more closely at the International

Scientific Unions. Although these number today a baker's
dozen, ranging from Astronomy through Chemistry to the
History and Philosophy of Science, the first urge of the scientists
of different nations to band together to further the advance of
their particular disciplines came from those whose laboratory
is the World: the astronomers, the geophysicists, and the radio-
scientists. And so you have a number of international scientific
clubs, the members of which are all known to each other per-
sonally, whose aim is to collaborate together in extending the
boundaries of knowledge in their own particular sphere of
activity in the exploration of the earth and its atmosphere. . . .
These are the people to propose.

On the other hand, the National Academies can tap the
financial and organisational resources of their respective countries. The National Academy of the United States can tap
the vast scientific potential of North America, the Académie des
Sciences de Paris can recruit the unbreakable genius of France,
the Royal Society of London can still squeeze funds out of
the British Treasury for a worthy object, the Academy of
Sciences of the U.S.S.R. has an apparently unlimited financial
backing.

Thus the International Council of Scientific Unions, poor
but proud, can indeed release a torrent of international scientific
activity: always provided that its demand exceeds the threshold
of national and international desire. Never can the Council
attempt to impose on its members a paper scheme, conceived
in the cloud-cuckoo-land of pious hopes, hatched out of the
egg of the ancient gnostic heresy of a heaven here on earth.

The march of events

So Chapman and Berkner, in 1950, put the ball square in the
court of the International Council of Scientific Unions. Meeting in Washington, D.C., in the fall of 1951, ICSU gave sanc-
tion to the formation of a small committee, not merely to explore, but to set in motion, the project of the International Geophysical Year 1957–58. No need for panels of experts—they
were all there on the spot, within the organisation. No call for
a board of advisers: the men who backed the advice of the

originators of the new idea were their own judges. . . . *Benjamin Franklin would have approved.*

Colonel Ernest Herbays, a regular officer of the Belgian Army, a radio-technician of the old school who knew all about how to get a good earth for a field aerial, was appointed the convenor of the first embryo committee which should frame the programme of the IGY. He called the first meeting of the special committee in his native city of Brussels in the autumn of 1952.

In 1953, twenty-three national committees had been formed under the ægis of the appropriate National Academies. Once again the ICSU committee met in Brussels, and this time it framed substantially the same programme as is being implemented today. At this meeting Chapman was elected President, Berkner Vice-President, and Marcel Nicolet, an acknowledged authority on the physics of the upper atmosphere, Secretary of the IGY. A secretariat was set up under Nicolet in Brussels, with the material help of the Belgian Government and with the generous financial backing of UNESCO.

In September 1954 the organising committee met in Rome, in the rooms of the Italian National Research Council. By now there were thirty-six national committees eager to contribute to the launch of the IGY. No one who was present at that gathering can ever forget the scene: of the great hall of the Consiglio Nazionale della Richerche di Italia, with its dado of Carrera marble, its murals by Antonio Achilli: Galileo, Volta, Galvani, Marconi looking down on men of all nations—white, brown, yellow, Russians from Moscow and the Caucasus—working together with complete singleness of purpose to a common end.

In September 1955 the same men met together again, in the Palais des Académies in Brussels. Now there were forty national participants. Here all but the final details were thrashed out; but a new facet of the programme was the announcement of the United States satellite project.

Finally, in September 1956, in the spacious building of the Spanish National Research Council in Barcelona, came the last planning conference; and this time the Russians announced their own satellite project, so designed as to key in with the American techniques. . . . Fifty-four nations were now lined up for the IGY.

Co-ordination

That is today a much-abused word—along with some others, such as collaboration, co-operation, dissemination and cross-fertilisation. But with a serious effort of world-wide observation of natural phenomena in view, co-ordination of the individual national efforts is compulsory. And this was the principal business of those busy meetings in Brussels, Rome, and Barcelona: how to link the programmes put forward by the fifty-four nations with the general world-wide programme which would benefit them all.

A 24-hour watch on the sun

The first essential was to ensure a 24-hour watch on the sun. For, as we have seen, the year 1957–58 had not been chosen at random for a concerted attack on the characteristics of the earth's envelope: it is the current maximum in the cycle of solar activity, that waxes and wanes over an average period of 11 years. So among the key stations of the IGY are the Solar Observatories.

Thirty-eight solar observatories, girdling the earth, are lined up for intensive observation of the sun. And at many of them the astronomers are already working overtime, so that they may pass the baton of observation, like runners in a relay race, to their western neighbours, without a break in the chain. In the words of the formal recommendation of the organising committee: "The hours of watching in Western Europe should be continued until after eastern stations in America have started observing, and western stations in America should continue watching until after observations have started in Japan, Australia, and New Zealand."

The watch on the sun will register the occurrence of sunspots, prominences, outbursts of radio-noise: but above all the occurrence of solar flares. For we have seen in Chapter 5 that it is the solar flares, rather than the sunspots, which are responsible for instantaneous radio fade-outs, and the sudden enhancement of atmospherics—and, a day or so later, for great magnetic storms in the earth's atmosphere.

So observatories which are equipped for the photography of solar flares are all set for a continuous flare patrol during the hours of sunlight: every 30 seconds a photograph of the sun's disc will be taken through a special filter which reveals the outburst of a flare. In fact, so important is this flare patrol that many observatories have specially installed one or more automatic recorders of atmospherics, such as we described in Chapter 5, so that the occurrence of a flare on the sun may be registered when photography of the sun is hindered by cloud.

World alerts

Experienced solar observers can often guess from the first appearance of a disturbance on the sun whether it is likely to lead to a great magnetic storm in the earth's atmosphere. Thus the rotating sun may bring into view on the eastern edge of the sun's disc a sunspot which is typically flare-active in character. The observer watches it from day to day as it is carried westwards towards the centre of the sun's disc. He sums his observations of prominences, flares, magnetic fields; and forms a not unreliable judgement as to whether its arrival at the sun's centre will herald a magnetic storm on the earth.

An elaborate system of radio and telegraphic communication has been worked out to give upwards of 800 stations, equipped to observe the numerous phenomena which accompany magnetic storms, timely warning of such special events on the sun, so that the scientists manning them may be on the alert. It is at such times, too, that the launching of rockets, packed with apparatus for the observation of the overhead currents in the atmosphere, solar spectra, or the impact of corpuscles from the sun on the earth, is particularly profitable.

These warnings are known as World Alerts, and the job of issuing them has been assigned to the powerful radio transmitter at Fort Belvoir near Washington, on the basis of information received by radio from Paris, Moscow, and Tokio. A team of trained predictors of solar disturbances has been assembled at

Final Calendar of Regular World Days (RWD)
and World Meteorological Intervals (WMI)
during the
International Geophysical Year 1957-1958

(Adopted by CSAGI, September 1956 and edited by)
(CSAGI SECRETARIAT - 3, AVENUE CIRCULAIRE, UCCLE-BELGIUM)

World Meteorological Interval
| 20 | 21 | 22 |
| 23 | 24 | 25 | 26 | 27 | 28 | 29 |

Regular world day ⑪
Regular world day at new moon ⑩
Unusual meteoric activity _8 (but not world day)
Regular world day with unusual meteoric activity ⑰
Day of total eclipse 🔲12

June 1957 (Advance Trial)

Sun.	Mon.	Tue.	Wed.	Thu.	Fri.	Sat.
						1
2	3	4	5	6	7	_8
_9	10	11	12	13	14	15
16	17	18	19	20	21	22
23	24	25	26	㉗	㉘	㉙
30						

July 1957

Sun.	Mon.	Tue.	Wed.	Thu.	Fri.	Sat.
	1	2	3	④	5	6
7	8	9	10	11	12	13
14	15	16	17	18	19	20
21	22	23	24	25	㉖	㉗
28	29	30	31			

August 1957

Sun.	Mon.	Tue.	Wed.	Thu.	Fri.	Sat.
				1	2	3
4	_5	6	7	8	9	10
11	⑫	13	14	15	16	17
18	19	20	21	22	23	24
㉕	㉖	27	28	29	30	31

September 1957

Sun.	Mon.	Tue.	Wed.	Thu.	Fri.	Sat.
①	2	3	4	5	6	7
8	9	10	11	12	13	14
15	16	17	18	19	20	21
22	㉓	㉔	25	26	27	28
29	㉚					

October 1957

Sun.	Mon.	Tue.	Wed.	Thu.	Fri.	Sat.
		1	2	3	4	5
6	7	8	9	10	11	12
13	14	15	16	17	18	19
20	21	㉒	㉓	㉔	25	26
27	28	29	30	31		

November 1957

Sun.	Mon.	Tue.	Wed.	Thu.	Fri.	Sat.
					1	2
3	4	5	6	7	8	9
10	11	12	13	⑭	15	16
17	18	19	20	㉑	㉒	23
24	25	26	27	28	29	30

December 1957

Sun.	Mon.	Tue.	Wed.	Thu.	Fri.	Sat.
1	2	3	4	5	6	7
8	9	10	11	12	⑬	14
15	⑯	17	18	19	20	㉑
㉒	23	24	25	26	27	28
29	30	31				

The official calendar

January 1958

Sun.	Mon.	Tue.	Wed.	Thu.	Fri.	Sat.
			1	2	(3)	(4)
5	6	7	8	9	10	11
12	13	14	15	16	17	18
(19)	(20)	21	22	23	24	25
26	27	28	29	30	31	

February 1958

Sun.	Mon.	Tue.	Wed.	Thu.	Fri.	Sat.
						1
2	3	4	5	6	7	8
9	(10)	11	12	13	14	15
16	17	(18)	(19)	20	21	22
23	24	25	(26)	27	28	

March 1958

Sun.	Mon.	Tue.	Wed.	Thu.	Fri.	Sat.
						1/8
2	3	4	5	6	7	
9	10	11	12	13	14	15
16	17	18	19	(20)	(21)	22
23	24	25	26	27	(28)	29
30	31					

April 1958

Sun.	Mon.	Tue.	Wed.	Thu.	Fri.	Sat.
		1	2	3	4	5
6	7	8	9	10	11	12
13	14	15	16	17	(18)	19
(20)	21	22	23	24	25	26
27	28	29	30			

May 1958

Sun.	Mon.	Tue.	Wed.	Thu.	Fri.	Sat.
				1	2	3
4	(5)	6	7	8	9	10
11	12	13	14	15	16	17
(18)	(19)	20	21	22	23	24
25	26	27	28	29	30	31

June 1958

Sun.	Mon.	Tue.	Wed.	Thu.	Fri.	Sat.
1	2	3	4	5	6	7
8	(9)	10	11	12	13	14
15	16	(17)	(18)	19	20	21
22	23	(24)	25	26	27	28
29	30					

July 1958

Sun.	Mon.	Tue.	Wed.	Thu.	Fri.	Sat.
		1	2	3	4	5
6	7	8	9	10	11	12
13	14	15	(16)	(17)	18	19
20	21	22	23	24	25	26
(27)	28	29	30	31		

August 1958

Sun.	Mon.	Tue.	Wed.	Thu.	Fri.	Sat.
					1	2
3	4	5	6	(7)	8	9
10	11	(12)	13	(14)	(15)	16
17	18	19	20	21	22	23
24/31	25	26	27	28	29	30

September 1958

Sun.	Mon.	Tue.	Wed.	Thu.	Fri.	Sat.
	1	2	3	4	5	(6)
7	8	9	10	11	12	(13)
(14)	15	16	17	18	19	(20)
21	22	23	24	25	26	27
28	29	30				

October 1958

Sun.	Mon.	Tue.	Wed.	Thu.	Fri.	Sat.
			1	2	3	4
5	6	7	8	9	(10)	(11)
(12)	(13)	14	15	16	17	18
19	20	21	22	23	24	25
26	27	28	29	30	31	

November 1958

Sun.	Mon.	Tue.	Wed.	Thu.	Fri.	Sat.
						1
2	3	(4)	5	6	7	8
9	(10)	(11)	12	13	14	15
16	17	(18)	19	20	21	22
23/30	24	25	26	27	28	29

December 1958

Sun.	Mon.	Tue.	Wed.	Thu.	Fri.	Sat.
	1	2	3	4	5	6
7	8	9	(10)	(11)	12	(13)
14	15	16	(17)	18	19	20
(21)	22	23	24	25	26	27
28	29	30	31			

January 1959

Sun.	Mon.	Tue.	Wed.	Thu.	Fri.	Sat.
				1	2	(3)
(4)	5	6	7	8	(9)	(10)
11	12	13	14	15	16	17
18	19	20	21	22	23	24
25	26	27	28	29	30	31

of the IGY World Days.

Fort Belvoir, and successful rehearsals have already been staged in the spring of 1957. A World Alert is issued 4 to 6 days ahead of an expected disturbance on the sun at or near the centre of the sun's disc. If the disturbance continues to look important, then the day before its expected advent the Central Warning Service at Fort Belvoir flashes the pre-arranged signal "AGI–SSSSS–SWI", indicating that a Special World Interval of several days will be observed. . . . Fort Belvoir also flashes an All Clear when the solar disturbance is over.

In this way, observers up and down the world—of radio fade-outs, atmospherics, geomagnetic effects, earth currents, and displays of the aurora—can conserve their energies for periods of maximum solar-terrestrial activity, and then go all out towards constructing a real world picture of the event, not only in relation to the geographical map of the world, but also in relation to the sequence of events which are taking place high above the earth's surface.

RWD's and WMI's

Apart altogether from the short-term prediction of exceptional events on the sun, with the consequent announcement of Special World Intervals, there is a regular calendar of concentrated observation, which aims once again at the same time to conserve and to concentrate the energy of the observers. The IGY Calendar pinpoints Regular World Days (RWD), World Meteorological Intervals (WMI), days of unusual meteoric activity, and days of total eclipse.

The Regular World Days occur twice a month—two days together at each new moon, and a single day at quarter moon. These days are set apart for intensive observations of all kinds. Then every quarter comes a period of 10 days during which the meteorologists will aim to be especially active, mapping the current trends of wind and weather at each equinox and solstice. Next come days of enhanced meteoric activity, when the radio-astronomers in particular, in conjunction with their radio-astronomical colleagues, will try to pin down once and for all the elusive phenomenon of "Sporadic E", which we have touched on in Chapter 4. . . . And finally there are days of total eclipse, during which the radio-scientists will be more than usually busy. The total eclipse of October 23, 1957 will be observable only in Antarctica; that of April 19, 1958 will be an annular eclipse visible in South-east Asia; and that of October 12, 1958 will be visible in the South Pacific.

World panorama

Baker Lake, Coral Harbour, Buffalo, Cape Hatteras, Huancayo, Sao Paulo, Port Lockroy, Vahsel Bay: Tromsö, Lerwick, Jungfraujoch, Pic du Midi, Kano, Fernando Po, Walvis Bay; Okhotsk, Kyoto, Taipei, Guam, Alice Springs, Terre Adélie.

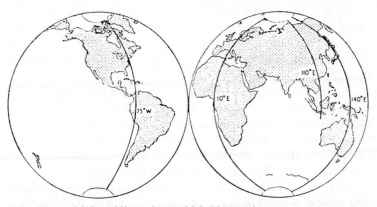

The three chief meridians along which IGY stations are strung out from Pole to Pole. Besides these, a fourth has been added, at 110° E., to give additional coverage for the Soviet Union and South-east Asia.

These are the names of a few of the hundreds of observation stations, strung like beads from Pole to Pole along the three strategic meridians of the International Geophysical Year: 75° W., 10° E., 140° E. Some of these, of course, are well-established observatories of long standing, others are easy enough of access, but quite a few demanded real pioneering work in their establishment and manning. But the organising committee for the IGY has encouraged every participating country along these pole-to-pole chains to fill in all the gaps: so that for the first time in history simultaneous observations in meteorology, geomagnetism, and ionospherics can be made in all latitudes.

But the scientists co-operating in the IGY will also put girdles round the earth—in the Arctic, in the Equatorial Belt, and in the Antarctic. It is of special importance for observations on the wide range of phenomena associated with magnetic storms that attention should be concentrated *simultaneously* on the northern and southern auroral zones; and equally on the equatorial zone, high above which is supposed to flow the great ring current of charged particles from the sun.

In the Arctic there are already many permanent scientific observatories—in Northern Canada, in Greenland, in Scandinavia, and in the U.S.S.R.—as a result of the modern possibilities of airborne traffic, of several kinds, over the north polar cap. So, paradoxically, these inhospitable regions were already tolerably well equipped to take part in the peaceful programme of the IGY.

The Equatorial Belt needed more attention, particularly because of the enormous stretches of open ocean, which have lonely islands as the only possibility for the setting up of special stations over thousands of miles of the equatorial girdle. So we find Dio Garcia, Minicoy, Addu Atoll in the Indian Ocean; Ino Jima, Truk, Eniwetok, Finafuti in the Pacific. . . .

Antarctica is of course in a class apart. It has been estimated that around a third of the total cost of the whole IGY has gone to the opening up of a region which, as Chapman has put it, we know less about than we do about the moon.

The story of the IGY in Antarctica deserves its own chapter.

Mountains in Antarctica, photographed from the air during the late Admiral Byrd's expedition of 1946–47.

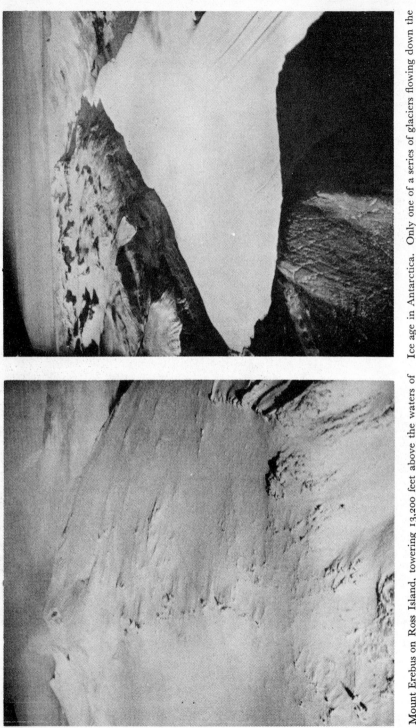

Mount Erebus on Ross Island, towering 13,200 feet above the waters of McMurdo Sound, crowned by a plume of volcanic steam.

Ice age in Antarctica. Only one of a series of glaciers flowing down the valleys from the mountains of the west coast.

CHAPTER 7

ANTARCTICA

Facts

ANTARCTICA is the sixth great land-mass of the world. It is a continent of approximately 5 million square miles—nearly twice as large as Australia—lying practically wholly within the Antarctic Circle, with the South Pole almost at its centre.

It is a mountainous region, rising steeply from the coast in most areas, with peaks as high as 15,000 feet—comparable, that is, with Mont Blanc—some of which, like Mount Erebus in the Ross Sea, are active volcanoes. But the South Pole itself is on a high, windless plateau, where powder snow lies unbroken above hundreds of feet of compacted ice.

Antarctica is the coldest and windiest region of the whole globe. It is far colder than the Arctic, where the relatively thin ice over the Arctic Ocean allows warming of the atmosphere from below. The air above Antarctica has no such central-heating system. It lies over a massive continent, glacier-bound, literally in an ice age; and temperatures of 100° below freezing can result. Surface winds, funnelled down the glacial valleys from the interior, beat north at speeds of 100 miles an hour near the coasts. . . .

And of course for months in the year it is dark. The antarctic winter is the northern summer, and so at midsummer's day in the north there is black night within the Antarctic Circle. Owing to the extreme cold, however, the antarctic night is far more severe than in the Arctic; so much so that the insulating roof of the troposphere seems to disappear altogether in the antarctic mid-winter, leaving the lower atmosphere open to outer space.

The seas about the Antarctic Continent are icebound for the greater part of the year. At the close of the antarctic winter the frozen ice-pack may extend northwards for hundreds of miles

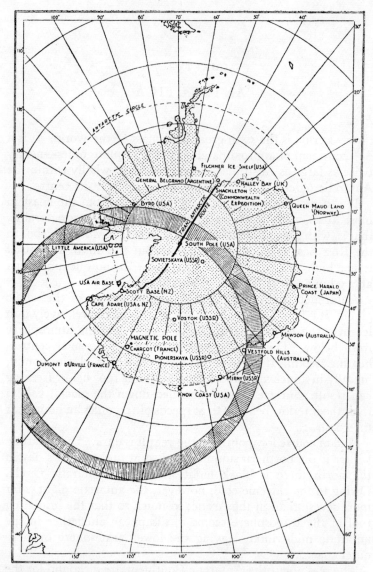

Antarctica: showing the siting of the observational stations for the first
scientific exploration of the continent; the route of the Commonwealth
trans-antarctic expedition; and the auroral zone of the aurora australis.

off the coast. Only in late summer can free access to the coast be expected. That is why expeditions to the Antarctic sail from ports in the northern hemisphere in the month of November.

Antarctic telescope

In Antarctica in 1957–58 the two ages of exploration—geographical and scientific—are uniquely telescoped. The urge that has sent expeditions from Australia, Belgium, France, Japan, New Zealand, Norway, the United Kingdom, the United States, and the U.S.S.R. to Antarctica is certainly not political, only incidentally geographical, and overwhelmingly for the purpose of scientific exploration.

Yet the fact remains that more than 3 million square miles of the continent remain unexplored geographically, and therefore one can expect a wealth of topographical information about Antarctica to be won, although one might say accidentally, by the expeditions which have set out as part of the world-wide programme of scientific exploration of the International Geophysical Year.

The Commonwealth Expedition, which plans to traverse the continent from Vahsel Bay to the Ross Sea, is in a different category altogether. Its aim is primarily that of all former expeditions to Antarctica: geographical exploration motivated by high physical endeavour. This thrusting expedition, as contrasted with the establishment of observational stations which is the job of the others, may well bring back priceless information as to whether Antarctica is truly one land-mass, or two adjacent islands separated by a channel. But that information is geographical information, with perhaps extra scientific information on the side. It could be garnered next year, or the year after, or five years hence: it is not imperative that it be obtained in a year of sunspot maximum. This is, however, quite crucially the case for the antarctic expeditions of the age of scientific exploration. Moreover, these expeditions will be working in conjunction with men of all nations who will be taking simultaneous observations of the earth's environment on the floating ice of the Arctic Seas, in Alaska, Siberia, Japan; on observatories high in the Andes, in equatorial Africa, in Indonesia; or in Chile, South Africa, and Australia.

Scientific exploration

Why, then, are men of so many nations eager to immure themselves on this inhospitable, nay hostile land-mass for two whole years, for the sole purpose of sitting in one unglamorous spot in order to take observations, day after day and month after month, of wind and weather, the earth's magnetic field, the aurora australis, cosmic rays, and the twinkling of radio-stars?

The answer is that without them the world programme of concentrated observation of our environment, carried out at a peculiarly opportune period of the solar cycle that determines so many of the happenings within the gaseous envelope of the earth, would be woefully incomplete. . . . Let us particularise.

Antarctic meteorology

Here are some of the questions to be answered about meteorological conditions in the Antarctic, which are bound to affect the global circulation of the earth's atmosphere, a problem in the fuller understanding of the earth's climate and weather which we have already touched on in Chapter 2 of this book.

Does the atmosphere above Antarctica take an active part in the general circulation, or is it for the most part sealed off from the rest of the atmosphere? Are the circumpolar long waves in the westerlies around the South Pole an important influence in Antarctica, or are pressure waves radiating from Antarctica a factor of greater significance in the general circulation? Is the geographical South Pole also the South Pole of the atmospheric circulation? How does the atmosphere operate to achieve almost perfect radiation balance? How are we to measure the precipitation over the Continent, so as to distinguish between fallen and drifting snow?

These are some of the questions posed by Harry H. Wexler, Chief of the Scientific Division of the United States Weather Bureau, and the man primarily responsible for the Weather Central at Little America on the shores of the Ross Sea, which

Deep crevasses in the ice of a glacier on the slopes of the 15,000-feet-high
Mount Markham.

The Russian ships, the *Ob* and the *Lena*, make landfall near the U.S.S.R. base at Mirny.

A general view of Mirny base.

is to serve the stations of all the nations which have converged on Antarctica in the interests of scientific exploration. The task of the central bureau is threefold: first to assemble, analyse, and transmit its meteorological observations for the use of all; second, to conduct research into the atmospheric conditions in the Antarctic; third, to assist all other stations, of whatever nationality, in their own investigations into the conditions in the atmosphere above Antarctica, and to issue warnings of the imminence of unusually bad weather... And here there are two points which deserve mention: one, the peculiar difficulty of radio-communications in polar regions; and second, the horrid "white-out".

Radio cut-offs

The southern auroral zone, centred about the South Magnetic Pole, cuts right across the Antarctic Continent. Hence at any time radio communication between distant points on the continent is difficult enough, owing to the extra ionisation in the reflecting layers of the ionosphere which accompanies displays of the aurora—a phenomenon well enough known already in military circles in Northern Canada. But in 1957–58—in the very year chosen for its highest solar effects on the earth's atmosphere, the corresponding advent of great magnetic storms, exceptional auroral displays, maximum ionospheric disturbances—the difficulties of radio communication are immense. Even in the preliminary stages of the Antarctic operation, communication between the Royal Society Base at Halley Bay and the Commonwealth Expedition at Shackleton, only 220 miles apart, has been easier via Port Lockroy in South Georgia than from station-to-station direct.

These difficulties were effectively ironed out at an historic conference on the Antarctic, held in Paris in July of 1956, presided over by that redoubtable Frenchman Georges Laclavère. A system, feminine not because of French predilection, but on account of the gender of the word "Station", was established: of "Mother Stations", "Daughter Stations", and "Granddaughter Stations", which should largely surmount the majority of the ionospheric obstacles.

White-outs

In the days of dog-teams, ponies, and man-hauled sledges, nobody bothered much about white-outs. But today, when polar transport, north or south, depends markedly on aircraft, either skid-landing or helicopter, this curse of the polar regions is a genuine menace.

Every aviator, past or present, knows what agony it is to fly without modern instruments in cloud, where the friendly circular horizon is obscured, and one literally cannot know if one is to emerge right-side-up or upside-down. That is often the predicament of the reconnaissance aircraft-pilot over Antarctica, briefed perhaps to find a landing-place for heavy freight-carrying planes; or of the man sent out from base to succour a lost contingent on the ground. The high cloud overcast can cause such a high degree of diffusion of the down-coming sunlight on to the blinding white wastes below that all shadows disappear: the whole landscape is swathed in a misty white light: all contours are gone: the horizon is gone. All is a dreary white featureless dream—and another aircraft crashes.

In the official language of the Paris Conference:

> "In the absence of snow blown by the wind, during a period of complete overcast over a terrain totally covered by snow, the contours of the region can vanish completely, all shadows disappear, and the horizon can no longer be distinguished."

When these meteorological conditions are predicted over any area, the United States Weather Central flashes the warning: WHOUT.

Hydrogen

Of primary importance in the heavy cargoes of equipment carried south of 75° for the Geophysical Year in the Antarctic, is the lightest of all gases—hydrogen. For it is hydrogen that fills the balloons which tell the meteorologists about the atmospheric conditions aloft, that enables them to calculate, predict, or sometimes guess at the weather situation at ground level. Hence the understandable chagrin at the loss of all

the hydrogen-making chemicals carried south by the advance
party of the Commonwealth Expedition, sunk below the broken
pack-ice on which they had been hastily parked. The gallant
inhabitants of the Sno-cat packing-case left behind by the ice-
thwarted *Theron* were thus left dependent for a full year on
information from the Royal Society base at Halley Bay, on
Little America, and on the Russian base at Mirny across the
continent, for their weather information. . . . Hydrogen is vital
to weather warnings in Antarctica.

The earth's magnetic field

The South Magnetic Pole lies in Antarctica, 1,400 miles
from the geographical South Pole. Now the South Magnetic
Pole is not only so close to the Geographical Pole, the southern
terminus of the three key meridians 35° W., 10° E., and 140° E.;
it is also the centre of the antarctic auroral zone. So at or near
this point on the Continent the following problems are of first
importance: the mapping of the earth's magnetic field aloft, the
tracking of displays of the aurora australis, and observations
on the cosmic rays, which we shall have more to say about in
the next chapter.

We have seen in Chapter 4 that the conjectural picture of the
great magnetic storms, that follow a day or so after the outburst
of a powerful solar flare, demands the appearance around the
North and South Magnetic Poles of particles of atomic hydrogen, thrown out from the equatorial current ring, and guided
with ever-increasing velocity along the lines of force of the
earth's magnetic field, which of course converges on the magnetic poles. Hence the importance of studying the whole
synoptic picture of a great magnetic storm at or near the South
Geo-magnetic Pole, in close conjunction with observers within
the Arctic Circle. So instruments to detect the electric currents
in the upper atmosphere, which the theory demands—sheets
of charged particles circling the Magnetic Pole to give current
strengths of hundreds of thousands of amperes—are part of
the cargo carried south. So also are instruments for measuring
the earth currents which are induced by an overhead current
system such as the observers expect to find.

Aurorae

All-sky cameras will be set up on the Antarctic Continent to photograph the aurora australis, once every 5 to 15 minutes, all through the long months of the polar night. Patrol spectrographs, automatically scanning the auroral displays, will make records of their spectral lines, which are a tell-tale of the molecular and atomic species in the upper atmosphere. And of course there will be the trained eyes of the scientists recording the changing forms of the shimmering arcs, rays, and curtains as the displays wax and wane.

Never before have systematic observations on the aurora australis been made in or near the southern auroral belt—the radio operator's nightmare is the auroral expert's picnic. And the auroral observers need not only relish this new opportunity of the first intensive study of the aurora australis. They have the added excitement of knowing that away in the north their colleagues are making simultaneous observations of the aurora borealis or "Northern Lights".

This matter of simultaneous observations north and south deserves our closer attention. We have seen that the auroral zones, north and south, encircle the Magnetic Poles. Hence corresponding points in the auroral zones are found, not at points on one of the earth's *geographical* meridians equidistant from the north and south geographical poles, but at opposite ends of a line of force of the earth's magnetic field. Thus for example the British observers at Halley Bay will link with their Canadian opposites in Newfoundland, the Americans at Little America with their colleagues at Baker Lake, and the Russians at Mirny with observers in Fridjof Nansen Land. In this way, a north–south symmetry in the displays of the aurora borealis and the aurora australis can be checked, as also whether the displays north and south occur simultaneously or not: with the strong hope that the whole mechanism of the mysterious aurora will be at least better understood, if not wholly explained, by the close of the year 1958.

The Americans in Antarctica and the Canadians in the far north have also planned the simultaneous observation of "whistlers" at opposite ends of a magnetic line of force, as an interesting sideshow in the auroral programme. One can picture the excitement with which they will afterwards compare their records, looking for 2 : 4 : 6 : 8 sequences in the south to match 1 : 3 : 5 : 7 sequences in the north, and vice versa!

The ionosphere above Antarctica

We have already touched on the practical difficulties of radio-communication in the Antarctic. From the scientific point of view, however, intensive observation of the conditions in the ionosphere, not only within the southern auroral belt, but above an enormous intensely cold land-mass which is in darkness for half the year, is at once a unique opportunity and a stimulating challenge. Such questions as these clamour for answer: Is the layer structure of the ionosphere over the south polar cap symmetrical with that already studied in some detail in the Arctic? Do the magnetic storms in the ionosphere in the south follow the same pattern as those in the north? How do the peculiar meteorological conditions over the continent affect the upper atmosphere? . . . These are no mere academic queries, either, for firm answers would have a profound influence on the technique of radio-communication in the southern hemisphere.

Twinkling stars

On November 15, 1956, a ship sailed from the Port of London bound for Shackleton and the Royal Society base at Halley Bay in the Weddell Sea. The *Magga Dan* carried in its hold, among many tons of scientific equipment, a quantity of complicated electronic gear for the observation of the scintillation of certain radio-stars south of 75°.

The twinkling of the stars which we can see with our own eyes on a clear frosty night is due to the wavering motion of the water vapour in the lower regions of the atmosphere, which allows passage of the light from the stars to reach us, looking up from below, now Yes now No. But there is another brand of star, that sends out radio-waves on the very short wave-band centred about a wave-length of one metre, which is invisible to our eyes, yet twinkles in its signals to an aerial tuned to its own wave-length, just as the visible stars scintillate in our unaided field of vision. The cause of the scintillation of radio-stars lies far above the water-vapour of the troposphere: it is situated in the waxing and waning of the clouds of electrified particles high aloft in the ionosphere, which say Yes–No to the passage of radio-waves from outer space.

The observation of the twinkling of radio-stars can in this way give us invaluable information about the ionospheric conditions aloft. But the physical difficulties, in the inhospitable Antarctic, are immense. They involve the erection of three large groups of aerials, half a mile apart, which require no less than 240 secure anchorages in the deep snow and ice of Halley Bay.

Nevertheless, this project is being attempted. The radio source lies in the direction of the constellation Centaurus, marking the spot where two cosmic galaxies collided tens of millions of light-years ago: an ancient cataclysm which is used today to find out more about the earth's upper atmosphere. And here comes the important point: that the records of the twinkling of this radio-source, caused by clouds of charged particles in the ionosphere, viewed far away in the Antarctic waste, will be duplicated by simultaneous observations at Jodrell Bank near Manchester, in order that a tolerably complete picture may be drawn of the variations in the electrical conditions in the ionosphere during the fierce magnetic storms that can confidently be anticipated during the maximum period of solar activity in the year 1957–58.

Glaciers yet again

Glaciers in the northern hemisphere are shrinking. In Scandinavia they are drawing back up the mountain valleys, in Greenland their ocean terminals break south in sea-borne ice, in Switzerland there is worry about future sources of water-power. Is this trend world-wide, evidence of a slow warming of the whole earth? Here Antarctica can perhaps answer at any rate the last of these pressing questions. For around 90 per cent of the total ice-cover of the world lies on the southern continent —the glaciers of the rest of the earth are an insignificant 10 per cent. Thus a determination of the direction of the trend of the expected shrinkage in the antarctic ice—which may of course turn out to be a confirmation of its stability—is of more than merely academic interest to mankind; for wastage of *all* the enormous ice-sheet of Antarctica would raise the average sea-level all over the world by nearly 200 feet. This might conceivably happen in say 10,000 years; but an initial rise in the average sea-level of, say, 30 feet in 10 years is not impossible.

Trends as protracted as these cannot be traced during the sojourn in Antarctica of less than two years of the dedicated scientists of ten nations. But a beginning can be made. So measurements of the ice thickness of the antarctic glaciers is one of the items on the programme of this particular chapter of the International Geophysical Year. Such measurements are made, in the language of the young men undertaking them, by "seismic shooting". This means that the investigator bores a deep hole in the ice, inserts an explosive charge, and measures the time of arrival of the artificial earthquake wave at a microphone sunk in another boring in the ice, perhaps 1,000 yards from the first. His records show him not only the time of arrival of the direct shudder through the ice, but also that of the tremor reflected from the firm ground below: so that he can find how deep is the ice-blanket above the continental mass below. Let us hope that they and their successors find the ice-cap of Antarctica to be stable!

Roll call

Who are the people who are agreed to inhabit the Antarctic Continent over the 1957–58 season in the interests of the world-wide programme of the IGY? Answer: Norwegians, Japanese, Australians, Russians, French, New Zealanders, Americans, British, Argentinians; and belatedly, but let us hope successfully, Belgians—not counting the cluster of surface meteorological stations on the Palmer Peninsula, manned by Argentinians, Chileans, and the British, nor the lonely island stations within the Antarctic Circle.

Let us call the roll, remembering that, with the exception of Norway and Japan (and now Belgium), all the other countries have been preparing the way ever since 1955, and that upwards of 300 men have already wintered in the Antarctic in 1955–56, as advance parties for the main contingents which converged on Antarctica late in the year 1956 for 1957–58.

Norway

On November 10, 1956, two sealing vessels, the *Polarsirkel* and the *Polarbjorn*, sailed from Oslo with the Norwegian Antarctic Expedition, led by the 36-year-old geodecist Sigurd Helle. They aim to make land as near the 10° E. meridian as possible in Queen Maud Land, where they will concentrate on meteorological observations.

Japan

Japan, like Norway, was a late starter. But in November 1956 the Science Council of Japan despatched the ice-breaker M/S *Soya* southwards to the Prince Harald Coast, to reconnoitre the site for a base and to establish a station where thirty scientists may carry out observations from February 1958 to January 1959, in nine of the recognised disciplines of the IGY programme.

Australia

On December 6, 1955, the chartered Danish vessel *Kista Dan*, 1,239 tons, sailed from Melbourne for Mawson Bay, where already an advance party had been established since February 1954. The *Kista Dan* duly arrived at Mawson in February 1956, and immediately began the routine of consolidation and reconnaissance which had been so carefully planned back in Melbourne.

Top priority was given to aerial surveys towards the auxiliary base at Vestfold Hills down the coast, slated for observations of the aurora australis during the IGY, in view of the specially favourable conditions at that site. In the course of these surveys, the Australians discovered a new mountain chain, with peaks up to 4,000 metres—equivalent, let us say, to the Matterhorn—extending for a distance of 320 kilometres south-west of Mawson. . . .

But perhaps the best way to flavour the spirit of this advance party is to quote at random from their official handbook.

"It should be remembered that the primary aim of the Mawson station is the collection of scientific data. . . . The successful completion of the scientific programme must be given first priority.

"*Hours of Duty.* Each member must be prepared to perform any duties allotted to him by the Officer-in-charge at any hour of the day or night. There are no fixed hours of duty and overtime will not be paid.

"*General Instructions.* Snow should be brushed from the clothes and boots before entering the huts, otherwise the interiors rapidly become wet. (A small hand-whisk should be hung in each porch for this purpose.)

"*Cook.* The Cook should make it continually his aim to infuse variety into the bill of fare at the Station. . . . He should not hesitate to make use of penguin, skua, seal, etc., for fresh meat, but should remember that these creatures are often infested with parasitical worms.

"*Safety.* Practise your rope technique before setting out. In particular, learn how to climb out of a crevasse up a rope without assistance.

"*Field Trips.* Anyone travelling on the sea-ice must travel with the assumption that the ice is liable to break out within the next twenty-four hours."

The U.S.S.R.

The Academy of Sciences of Moscow despatched two ships to the Antarctic from the Baltic in November 1955—the *Ob*, 12,500 tons, and the *Lena*, of about 5,000 tons. They arrived at the main base of Mirny, on the Knox coast, 300 miles from the Australian base, in January 1956, where they disembarked ninety-two people, four aircraft, two helicopters, four land-rovers, and tons of stores.

The Russians are mounting a fine programme. Apart from the main base, Mirny—which in Russian means "Peace"—they will have at least two advance stations, Sovietskaya and Vostock; also an auxiliary station, Pionerskaya, already established by the advance party in 1956.

Once again, here is a first-hand account, written in English by A. M. Gusev, a participant in the initial journey by sledge train from Mirny to Pionerskaya, which took place only some three months after the first landing, by which time a complete township of prefabricated huts had sprung up at the main base.

"The Council of the expedition adopted a suggestion of the leader of the expedition, M. V. Somov, to organise a sledge-tractor expedition to the interior of the continent. . . . Warm living quarters were built on one of the sledges, another held a galley and a dining room for three persons, not counting the man on duty. . . . The third sledge was intended for provisions and fuel, spare fur clothing and sleeping bags. . . .

"A compass was the only available means of showing the direction while the train was in motion. Therefore, a magnetic compass was installed in the living quarters and an observer who was connected by telephone with the tractor driver was always on duty near it when the train was on the move. . . .

"The expedition approached the 100th kilometre. Reconnaissance on AN 2 aircraft at the beginning of March showed that at this distance from the shore there were two regions with long, broad fissures stretching from south-west to north-east. . . . Often the expedition pushed on when visibility was low or even in darkness. Therefore on Somov's orders, the tractors were preceded by two men tied together with safety ropes. . . .

"Near the 150th kilometre, we were overtaken by an AN 2 aircraft. Our pilot, Lebedev, skilfully landed on an unprepared surface close to the habitable 'carriage'. Lebedev brought us news from Moscow, literature and fresh fruit. . . .

"Autumn was coming into its own: a violent snowstorm broke out in the evening of the same day that the aircraft made its departure. . . . In a few hours the train was snowbound. . . . It was only on April 19, when the storm began noticeably to abate, that we managed to free the train from its captivity and proceed on our way. . . .

"We were now 330 kilometres away from Mirny. By this

time we found ourselves up against new difficulties which prevented our progress: as a result of the very low temperature—59 to 52 below zero—the metal traces of the sledges began to burst and an attempt to replace them with ropes proved futile. The ropes snapped like thread. We had to lighten the load on the sledges as much as possible, throwing off a large number of empty fuel barrels that we used to mark every 25th kilometre, the reserve small shoes for the tractors, and the great quantity of snow that had accumulated on the sledges. . . . Slowly, we resumed our way. . . .

"Soon we received instructions from Somov to begin the construction of the first station on the Antarctic mainland. Between May 13 to 18 the separate parts of the sledge train were joined together. The resulting space between them was converted into an internal platform. An unheated, snow protected platform was also built. Thus, all the premises of the train were used for the station. Then an aerial mast was erected and the fitting out of grounds for various observations was started. . . .

"Because of inclement weather, great difficulties were encountered in bringing us supplies for the winter. But these were successfully surmounted. In view of the difficulty heavy aircraft had in landing, a considerable part of the supplies had to be dropped to us. First the aircraft brought us a supply of gas in cylinders for cooking food. These were all safely dropped. On the second trip the aircraft brought 40 cases of various provisions. These were dropped in the evening when visibility was low. We lit fires to guide the aircraft. On the next day we found all the 40 cases. . . .

"The polar night was closing in on us. On May 27, the sun no longer rose over the horizon. That day was fixed for the opening of the first inland station in the Antarctic Continent. It was named Pionerskaya."

France

The Norwegian vessel *Norsel*, Captain B. Jakobsen, sailed from Rouen in October 1955 and made land at Durmont d'Urville in Terre Adélie on January 1, 1956. The French are no strangers to Antarctica: under the leadership of the veteran explorer Paul Emil Victor they have had a look at penguins, seals, pack-ice, and have faced the bitter winds that blow from the South Pole, already in 1951. But this time, strongly reinforced, they are out for purely scientific spoils. Fourteen to twenty scientists, not all French, will inhabit the Durmont d'Urville base during the key period 1957–58. These men will be linked with their comrades at the northern terminus of the appropriate geomagnetic line of force, at Resolute Bay in Canada, for the simultaneous observation of auroral displays, magnetic storms, and the conditions aloft in the ionosphere.

But perhaps one of the most interesting aspects of the French endeavour is the forward station, named "Charcot", in the immediate area of the South Magnetic Pole, some 300 kilometres towards the Geographic Pole from the main station on the coast. Three men will stay at Charcot over the period 1957–58.

New Zealand

The New Zealand party in Ross Bay has a threefold task: first, to establish its own base at Scott Base in McMurdo Sound, for scientific observations in meteorology, geomagnetism, aurora, ionospherics, and seismology during the IGY; second, to co-operate with the Commonwealth Antarctic Expedition at Scott Base; third, to link with the Americans at Cape Adare, the Antarctic terminus of the United States air-lift based on New Zealand. It is a big programme for a small country.

United States

The United States antarctic programme is by far the most comprehensive of any. No less than six stations are scheduled for occupation during the IGY, apart from that at Cape Adare, shared with New Zealand.

The main base is at Little America, on the shores of the Ross Sea; here also is located the Weather Central, a meteorological service for all the expeditions, of whatever nation.

On Ross Island, opposite Little America in the Ross Sea, is the "Williams Air Operations Facility", an air-base for heavy aircraft.

Byrd Station, in Marie Byrd Land, is destined primarily for meteorological observations, above all towards proving the existence or otherwise of the northward surges of the atmosphere over the Antarctic Continent, which are suspected to have a marked influence on the world's weather. The station on the Knox Coast has a similar purpose, acting as a check on Byrd Station. The station on the Weddell Sea is on the edge of the southern auroral zone, as are also the Little America and Byrd stations, and is thus with these others cunningly placed for concerted observation of the aurora australis. And finally there is the Pole Station, at the geographical South Pole, where ionospheric observations may be taken throughout the long period of total darkness—a unique opportunity for studying conditions in the upper atmosphere when there is no direct radiation from the sun to ionise it, and for mapping the world-wide magnetic storms at a key point on the earth's surface.

The National Academy of Sciences in Washington is responsible for the scientific planning of this gigantic undertaking. But the logistics involved are so immense that the Academy early called on the United States Navy for help. The result is "Operation Deep Freeze", until his recent death under the overall command of the veteran American explorer Admiral Byrd.

As early as 1954–55, the 5,000-ton ice-breaker U.S.S. *Atka* reconnoitred the Antarctic from the Ross Sea eastward to the Weddell Sea, in order to recommend sites for the stations. The *Atka* found that the oft-visited Bay of Whales in the ice-barrier of the Ross Sea had disappeared, and that the break in the ice-shelf there had drowned most of the stores left behind by the United States expedition of 1947, including six DC 3 aircraft which it had been hoped to use again in 1957. The *Atka* found a new anchorage at Kainan Bay, 40 miles north-east of the old Bay of Whales. In reconnoitring Kainan Bay, a helicopter pilot was killed during a polar white-out, coming out of a turn nose down, crashing on the ice at 60 miles an hour. Kainan Bay is now in full use by the main United States expedition.

In 1955–56 came Operation Deep Freeze I, making final preparations for the great onslaught of 1957–58. Nine ships,

including the *Glacier*, 8,600 tons, the largest ice-breaker of the
United States Navy, carrying hundreds of men and a vast quantity of material—upwards of 30,000 tons of tractors, aircraft,
helicopters, prefabricated huts, ample food stores—descended
on the shores of the Ross Sea. Eight heavy aircraft—two Douglas Skymasters among them—were flown in direct from Christ-
church New Zealand, a distance of 2,500 miles, to find the
landing-strip on Ross Island duly prepared for them. Marie
Byrd Land was reconnoitred by sledge-trains, the coast surveyed by the ice-breakers, flights into the interior were carried
out, including a reconnaissance of the Pole Station.

All this vast preparation was carried out with extraordinary
tenacity and skill. Cargo-hauling at Little America was carried
out on a 24-hour basis over a period of 4 weeks; construction
work at the air-base on Ross Island was by 12-hour shifts.
Much of the levelling of the boulder-strewn terrain for the air-
strip was done by hand. . . . No doubt the naval personnel
found suitable words for the crazy scientists.

And here are two laconic extracts from the official reports,
which mirror the stark conditions of Antarctica more truly than
any highly coloured account.

"In preparation for tractor-train operations to the Byrd
Station, a trail reconnaissance party of eight men in two
Tucker Sno-Cats and one Weasel with navigational equip-
ment and a crevasse detector, departed the Little America
Station on January 14, 1956, to locate a trail to the Byrd
Station suitable for tractor use. The party reached the 380-
mile point before turning back because of equipment break-
downs and the lateness of the season.

"When the trail reconnaissance party was returning to the
Little America Station by air, the plane crash-landed and was
lost for seven days. In support of the air search, a tractor
train of four tractors went out 100 miles hauling diesel fuel,
avgas, and wanigans. After the successful completion of the
search, a second train of five tractors started toward the 380-
mile point, but halted and returned to the Little America
Station, when one of the tractors went through a crevasse at

the 110-mile point. . . . While furnishing logistic air support to the tractor train operations from the Little America Station to the prospective site of the Byrd Station, a De Haviland Otter aircraft became lost in bad weather and subsequently crashed on Edward VII Peninsula because of severe icing. Search and rescue measures were immediately initiated.

"There remained no aviators at the Little America Station to commence an air search, and two attempts were made to fly an Otter from McMurdo Sound. Neither attempt was successful because of weather conditions. The Otter and helicopters at McMurdo Sound were loaded aboard an ice-breaker for their transfer to the Little America Station.

"Air search commenced with a helicopter flight to a high altitude, in the hope of receiving a radio bearing. Search patterns were flown continuously by the Otter and helicopter, resulting in the downed aircraft's being located on the third day. The personnel were airlifted back to the Little America Station with only minor physical injuries."

Now, in the summer of 1957, the final operation, Deep Freeze II, is completing its assignment. Thereafter, upwards of 100 American scientists, with half that number of support personnel, will be left in the polar darkness of the antarctic winter, making their careful records of wind and weather, the aurora australis, and ionospheric phenomena throughout 1957–58.

United Kingdom

The British expedition is sponsored by the Royal Society of London, which is in fact responsible for the entire organisation and planning of the enterprise.

The advance party sailed from Southampton on November 22, 1955, in a chartered Norwegian vessel, the M.S. *Tottan*, 540 tons, and on January 6, 1956, found a suitable base on the shores of the Weddell Sea, subsequently named Halley Bay, near the northern boundary of the auroral zone, and close to the bases in the same area occupied by the United States, Argentina, and the Commonwealth Expedition. This bare statement hides a fine record of cunning seamanship, for the

Tottan was unaccompanied by even a single ice-breaker, and instead relied on the advice of a veteran of Shackleton's *Endurance* expedition of 1915, James Wordie (now Sir James), in its manœuvring among the Weddell Sea ice.

By January 16 unloading of stores, equipment, and prefabricated huts was complete. Paradoxically, the unloading was greatly hindered by the high temperature and consequent slushy surface snow, and was often carried out at night, when the surface was somewhat harder. The *Tottan* sailed north on January 22, leaving a party of ten men at Halley Bay, under the leadership of Surgeon Lieutenant-Commander David Dagleish, which included three scientists charged with the task of carrying out the preliminary scientific programme.

Jubilant reports were soon received in London, by wireless via the Falkland Islands, that Halley Bay was proving an ideal site for observation of the aurora. Interesting preliminary observations of the ionosphere were reported. A new range of hills, appropriately christened the *Tottan Mountains*, was discovered.

On November 15, 1956, the M.V. *Magga Dan*, chartered by the Commonwealth Expedition, sailed from the Port of London. It carried also the main Royal Society party of twenty-one men, together with their radio-star scintillation gear, radio-echo equipment for tracking meteors, and the new Decca wind-finding radar apparatus, all for installation and try-out at Halley Bay before the balloons go up on July 1, 1957.

The Commonwealth Expedition

The Commonwealth Expedition, whereby Dr. Fuchs sets out from Shackleton Base on the Weddell Sea, and Sir Edmund Hillary from Ross Island on the New Zealand side, to meet near the Pole and return together to the Ross Sea, is quite definitely not a part of the IGY programme, nor can it be expected to contribute greatly to it. It is an independent enterprise, guided by a zeal for geographical exploration, not by any properly oriented scientific compass. It will be fun to watch; it may even be glorious; but it is only very incidentally geophysics.

"Operation Deep Freeze". U.S. naval personnel laying pipe-lines from the ice-breaker "Eastwind" to the fuel storage tanks at Hut Point on the McMurdo Sound.

Warming up the engines of an R4D Douglas Skymaster at the U.S. Air Base on McMurdo Sound.

The M.S. *Tottan* ready to sail northwards from Halley Bay, January 22, 1956.

The advance party of the Royal Society Expedition erecting their pre-fabricated hut at Halley Bay on the Weddell Sea.

CHAPTER 8

DIVISION OF LABOUR

GEOPHYSICS is a single science—the science of the physics of the earth and its atmosphere. But no one man can command all the skills which are needed for the scientific exploration of his environment. So we find that the men and women who are actually carrying out the thousands of different observations called for in the overall programme of the International Geophysical Year tend to fall into a number of groups—astronomers, meteorologists, geomagneticians, and so on—each group intent on widening the knowledge already gained in his own particular scientific discipline.

The organisers of the IGY have therefore divided the work into ten main sections. These are: Meteorology, Oceanography, Glaciology; Ionospheric Physics, the Aurora, Geomagnetism, Cosmic Rays; Seismology, Gravity, and Latitudes and Longitudes.

The detailed schedules for these ten different scientific disciplines have been worked out with great care and skill by working parties of the leading technicians in each branch, partly by correspondence, but mainly in long sessions of concentrated argument and discussion at the annual meetings in Brussels, Rome, and Barcelona during the preparatory period 1953-56.

So in this chapter we shall be concerned with "all trades, their gear and tackle and trim": and some of the gear is novel, ingenious, and exciting.

Three degrees of urgency

The ten trades which we now set out to review are obviously not all of equal importance to the programme of the IGY. In fact, they fall into three classes: those which it is *essential* to ply most vigorously at a period of sunspot maximum, when the terrestrial effects of the sun's activity are at a peak; those which are *contributory* to the effort of those in the first class; and those which it is *convenient* to include on a world-wide scale at a time when special stations will in any case have been set up at hundreds of places over the entire globe.

In the first class are included all the scientific disciplines which are concerned with the investigation of the upper atmosphere—Ionospheric Physics, Aurora, Geomagnetism, Cosmic Rays. In the second class fall those disciplines which pursue the study of the earth's climate and weather—Meteorology (which in some of its aspects overlaps with the interests of the first class), Oceanography, and Glaciology. In the third class come methods of exploring the earth's crust and core—Seismology, Gravity, and Latitudes and Longitudes. . . .

All these considerations were, of course, most earnestly taken account of by the organisers of the IGY, and it is due to them, and the good sense of the scientists of all nations participating in the effort, that a well-balanced programme has been achieved.

Meteorology

Our all-too-brief study of the current problems of Meteorology, in Chapter 2 of this book, has already shown that one of the chief obstacles to a complete understanding of the world's weather is the lack of adequate data about the conditions aloft in the southern hemisphere, and particularly over the Antarctic Continent.

During 1957–58 there will be upwards of sixty meteorological stations in Antarctica and on the islands of the sub-antarctic ocean alone, which will link with the standard meteorological institutes of the southern hemisphere to give adequate meteorological coverage south of the Equator for the first time in history.

There is, however, a second area of relatively unexplored meteorological territory, which encompasses the whole globe: namely, the canopy of air above say 12 miles. During the IGY, and especially on Regular World Days, meteorologists all over the world will probe the atmosphere up to a height of 18 miles, using specially large balloons. Now the height of the troposphere at the Equator is, as we have seen, around 10 miles, at the Poles around 5 miles; so that these high-altitude balloons

will penetrate right into the stratosphere, seeking evidence for
or against the revolutionary idea that a part of the global circulation occurs above the roof of the troposphere.

We have seen that a complete understanding of the zonal
and meridianal flow-patterns in the atmosphere still eludes the
meteorologists. Hence the importance of making observations
of the winds aloft in all latitudes simultaneously. This need is
taken care of in the programme of the IGY by the three chains
of stations, extending from Pole to Pole along the three meridians 75° W., 10° E., and 140° E.

We know that the global circulation of the atmosphere is
powered by the sun. Hence a knowledge of the day-to-day
variations in the amount of solar energy absorbed by the earth
and its atmosphere is of great importance to a full solution of
the circulation problem. Here the astronomers take over, by
measuring the fraction of solar radiation reflected from the
atmosphere, which allows the meteorologists in their turn to
deduce the fraction which is absorbed.

The astronomers will measure the reflected fraction—technically known as the *albedo* of the earth—at a number of different stations on the globe, by observations on the ashen light of
the moon. This earth-light of the moon, which everyone has
seen as the old moon in the young moon's arms, is of course
doubly reflected sunlight, from earth to moon and back to
earth. Thus by tracking the day-to-day fluctuation in the earth-
light of the moon, at stations so strategically placed on the
earth's surface as to make it possible to do so throughout each
month, the corresponding variations in the earth's albedo can
be followed, and so finally the variations in the amount of
energy available to drive the global circulation.

Such, then, are some of the highlights of the meteorological
programme. The gigantic task of organising the work at the
hundreds of special stations, of ensuring the use of properly
standardised instruments, of assembling and correlating the
thousands of observations in standard form, and of the handling
and discussion of the results, is primarily the responsibility of
the World Meteorological Organisation, which has joined with
ICSU in this section of the IGY effort.

Oceanography

The chief aims of the oceanographic programme are two in number: measurement of the deep-sea currents in both the Atlantic and Pacific, and observations of changes in sea-level right through the year at island stations in all the oceans.

The urge to explore the deep ocean currents is twofold. First, it has been increasingly realised that successful long-range

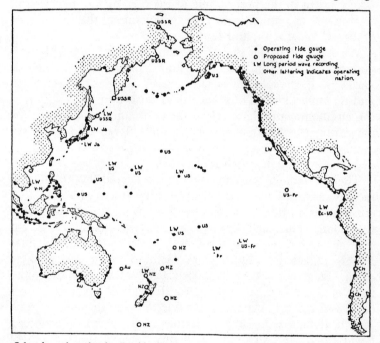

Island stations in the Pacific Ocean, at which sea-level changes and the passage of long waves will be recorded.

weather forecasting must depend, not only on a more thorough knowledge of the circulation of the atmosphere, but also on that of the oceans. Second, the age of the atomic energy power-station, already upon us, will be faced with the question whether it is really sensible to use the ocean-bed as a dump for the colossal quantities of radio-active waste which must be reckoned with in the future. The answer to this second question must

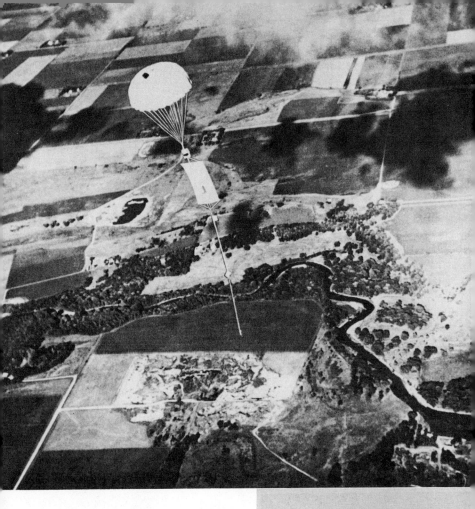

Instruments which have radioed meteorological information back to earth from a Skyhook balloon, descending by parachute so that they can do the same chore all over again.

The British "Decca" radar apparatus.

Radio signals from the searching disc are picked up and returned by a "corner reflector" attached to the balloon, in the same way as cats'-eyes reflect the light of a car's headlamps.

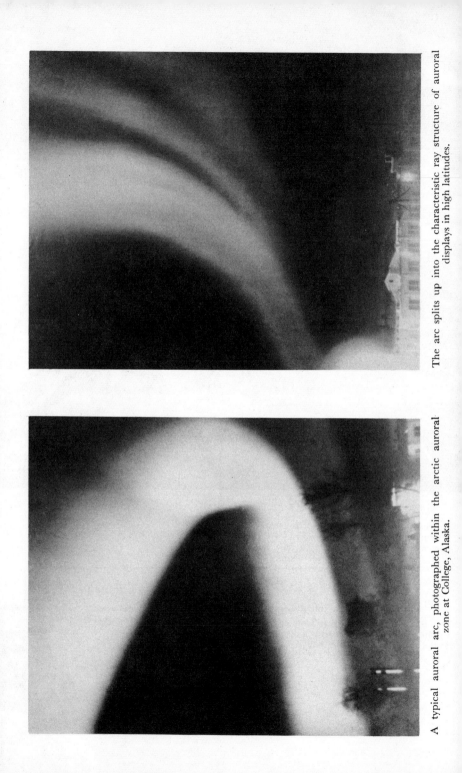

A typical auroral arc, photographed within the arctic auroral zone at College, Alaska.

The arc splits up into the characteristic ray structure of auroral displays in high latitudes.

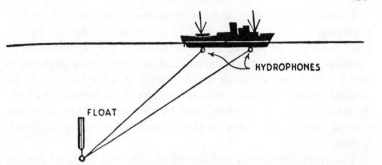

The Swallow float, consisting of a fasces of aluminium tubes which can be dimensioned so as to float under water at a chosen depth, carries a supersonic transmitter whose signals are received by two hydrophones let down from the survey vessel. The changing time-lag between the reception of these signals, first by one and then by the other of the ship's hydrophones, allows the drift of the float with the hidden currents to be determined.

depend on a knowledge of the rate of turnover of the ocean waters, which at the moment we don't possess: the rate may be so slow that large areas of the ocean could be poisoned; if rapid enough, then the dispersion of the radio-active waste might be so complete as to be harmless.

The Van Dorn long-wave recorder. The two capillaries, the bellows, and the standpipe are so proportioned that the bellows responds only to the long waves and not to the short waves or tides. The motion of the bellows is recorded by an electrical potentiometer.

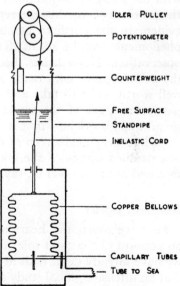

The island stations scheme is quite simply the logical method of solving the problems, at once of the seasonal changes in sea-level, which must betoken the end result of the deep-water circulation, and of the true character of the long waves in the open ocean which, as we have already seen in Chapter 3, can be masked by the subsidiary effects brought about by the relatively shallow continental shelves, and by the local effects of reflection of these long waves at the shore-lines of the great land-masses.

Two very intriguing instrumental aids will be used for the first time to any significant extent during the IGY: the Swallow float, a sort of submarine balloon which will hold itself indefinitely at a constant depth below sea-level; and the Van Dorn long-wave recorder, that forgets the tides and the wind-waves, and remembers only the long waves with a period between crest and crest of 5 to 15 minutes.

Glaciology

This is a long-term programme, comparable in this respect with the study of earthquakes and gravity. No final answer to the problem of whether the retreat of the glaciers already quite evident in the northern hemisphere is a regional or a global phenomenon can be got in 18 months of even the most intense observation. Nevertheless, because of the immense activity in the polar regions, both north and south, during the IGY, it is well worth while to take a closer look at the glaciers in those particular areas of the world. In a word, the glaciological programme is *epochal*—that is, you take advantage of the widespread geographical sweep of the IGY programme to make the first detailed survey of the glaciers of the whole world, to be repeated at an interval of, say, 10 or 20 years.

Ionospheric physics

Here we touch the heart of the whole IGY venture. For on account of the tight solar control of the ionosphere, which we have already dealt with in Chapter 4, we may surely hope that an intensive global study of the ionised layers of the atmosphere, during a year of maximum eruptive activity on the sun, will lead to an altogether new understanding of their ever-changing characteristics.

Moreover, this is no mere academic inquiry, although for many of the scientists concerned the how and the why of the thing are all-sufficient. Smooth and uninterrupted radio-communication must depend in the latter end on our ability to *predict* the changes in the reflecting power of the ionised layers for radio-waves of all frequencies.

There are already seventy-five stations, scattered over the globe, which make daily routine soundings of the height of the various layers of the ionosphere—E, F_1 and F_2. This they do by stabbing the ionosphere aloft with a train of short pulses of radio-waves, on a descending scale of wave-lengths, and recording the radio-echoes at an adjacent receiver. The interval of time between the transmission and reception of a pulse decides the height of the appropriate reflecting layer: the shorter the wave-length in the pulse the higher the reflecting layer. During the IGY the number of these "ionosonde stations" will be increased to 150, and the number of soundings of the upper air will be stepped up from hourly to quarter-hourly observations during the Special World Intervals.

Apart from this enhancement of the normal radio-sonde service, however, a whole group of techniques will converge on the problem of *horizontal movements* in the ionosphere—drifts of the free electrons, and winds transporting neutral and ionised particles alike across the roof of the atmosphere.

The standard method of observing winds in the ionosphere makes use of the fact that the reflecting surface of any ionised layer is not perfectly smooth, so that the strength of a radio-echo received from it on the ground depends on whether it comes from a high or a low point on the irregular surface of the ionised layer above. If now the whole layer is moving before a wind, fluctuations in the strength of the echo will be observed at a fixed point on the ground, according as a high or low point in the reflecting surface is passing overhead. So we have only to arrange a triangle of radio-receivers, spaced say 100 yards apart, with a single transmitter at the centre, and watch for a repetition of the fading pattern observed at one of them at another down-wind from the first, to determine the speed and direction of the ionospheric wind.

The snag in this method is that it is difficult to distinguish between a mass movement of an irregular layer above, moving before an ionospheric wind, and a steady undulatory motion of the reflecting surface—a wave-motion, in fact—which could well give the same fading pattern below. Two closely related methods of tracking winds in the ionosphere will therefore be more widely used than ever before during the IGY.

The first uses the twinkling of radio-stars, the variation in the strength of very short-wave radio-signals received from sources of radio-noise in outer space, such as may be caused by the ancient collision of two star galaxies. Once again, three such short-wave receivers, acting in unison, can track the downwind drift of the ionised particles aloft.

The second uses the radar-echoes from meteor trails. For if the trail of ionised particles behind an inward-rushing meteor is not formed in still air, it will drift down-wind, just like the vapour trail behind a jet aircraft on a boisterous day. The effect on the radar-echo is a rise in pitch if the wind is blowing the meteor trail towards the receiver, a drop in pitch if the meteor trail is blown away from the receiver.

At least two further methods of tracking winds in the lower reaches of the upper atmosphere are on the IGY programme, both involving the use of rockets—one of which depends on the explosion of rocket-borne grenades, the other on the ejection from a rocket of a canister of flaming sodium. But that is another story, to be told in the next chapter.

Fifty to sixty miles above earth, as we have learned in Chapter 4, lies the region of photo-dissociation—the "chemosphere", as it is often called—whose composition and movement are revealed pre-eminently by the night airglow. The airglow will be studied synoptically, on a global scale, during 1957–58. Sensitive spectrographs and photometers have been installed at upwards of a hundred stations in all latitudes, ready to observe the same phenomena in the same ways at the same time. The result can only be an altogether closer appreciation of the whole mechanism of the airglow, when the thousands of observations are eventually all analysed together.

The Aurora

The aurora is, as we already know, the outward and visible sign of the arrival of fast-moving charged particles from the sun in the upper atmosphere.

The aurora will be under simultaneous and co-ordinated observation in both hemispheres, by a variety of different methods, from July 1, 1957, to the close of the year 1958.

A novel device of astonishing simplicity, which has been produced in quantity for the IGY, is the Gartlein All-sky Camera. The primitive form of this instrument consists of a cine-camera, timed to take pictures every 5 minutes, mounted on a tripod above a convex lens, in which the reflection of the whole sky from horizon to horizon is visible. . . . That, and nothing more.

But consider the implications of its widespread use. First and foremost, at any one point on the earth it provides a permanent continuous record of the fantastically complicated changes in the shimmering arcs and rays and curtains of the auroral displays, which even the most trained observer finds it well-nigh impossible to follow with the naked eye, far less describe in scientific terms. Second, it allows comparison of records made by other cameras at other stations, taking pictures of the same display. And third, it allows the subsequent matching of records taken simultaneously in the two hemispheres, of the aurora borealis in the north and the aurora australis in the south: say at College in Alaska and on McQuarrie Island in the Antarctic, or at Little America and at Baker Lake in northern Canada, or at Naryan-Mar in northern Siberia and Heard Island in the South Seas. It is indeed an exciting prospect.

On nights when cloud obscures the northern or the southern sky within the auroral zone, the aurora can still be tracked, although not in the same detail, by the cat's eye of radar. Just as a radar-beam can guide a ship into harbour in fog, the same beam can "see" the reflecting electrified curtain of the aurora, and make a record of its changing shape and form. So also can the twinkling of radio-stars, viewed through the auroral curtain, give information about its formation and dispersion on nights when visual observation is impossible.

Visual observations, without any instruments, will play a part in the watch on the aurora during the IGY. For 1957–58 is, after all, a year of sunspot maximum, when auroral displays may be expected far south (and north) towards the Equator during the great magnetic storms that follow the outburst of flares on the sun. In these lower latitudes, the mere well-authenticated record of an auroral display, without any details of its form or colour, may be of use in the job of piecing together the overall picture of the consequences of magnetic storms which must be undertaken on the conclusion of the IGY. So the help of a great number of visual observers has already been enlisted: crews of commercial aircraft, captains of whaling vessels in the southern seas, amateurs in the United States, Canada, Great Britain, and the U.S.S.R.

Good luck to them all! But at the same time let us hope that the countries in the equatorial belt, which are participating in the 1957–58 effort, will organise visual observations of the aurora, at least during the Special World Intervals, when there is a flare-active spot near the centre of the sun's disc.

Geomagnetism

The geomagnetic field of the earth has been under continuous observation for over 100 years: but these observations refer principally to the slow variations arising from the turbulent motions in the liquid core of the earth, which have been already described in Chapter 1.

The geomagnetic observations during the IGY, on the other hand, will concentrate on the extremely rapid variations in the magnetic characteristics of the upper atmosphere, particularly during the great magnetic storms which follow the outburst of flares on the sun. These magnetic storms, as we already know, lead to world-wide disturbance of radio-communication, often to dislocation of ordinary compass navigation, and also to the appearance of exalted auroral displays.

The normal world network of geomagnetic observatories, some forty in number, will be doubled during the 18 months of the Geophysical Year, chiefly by an extension of the net in southern latitudes, and by an additional concentration in the equatorial belt. The number of measurements of the magnetic field at ground-level will be stepped up throughout the extended network, from three-hourly to quarter-hourly intervals.

From a subsequent analysis of this enormous mass of data, it may be expected that more will be learned about the pattern of the electrical currents aloft during magnetic storms than ever before. But the highest hopes are placed on rockets, held in reserve for use during the Special World Intervals, which even in their brief time of flight of 2 or 3 minutes can measure the magnetic and electrical characteristics of the upper atmosphere directly and *in situ*, while a magnetic storm is actually in progress.

Cosmic rays

We have already learned that the most probable cause of magnetic storms in the upper atmosphere is the arrival of charged particles of hydrogen shot out from the solar flares that accompany the appearance of sunspots on the solar disc.

But quite apart from this sporadic bombardment from the sun, the earth is under fire, night and day, all the year round, by much faster particles which arrive equally from all directions in space. These are the well named *Cosmic Rays*.

The cosmic rays are the nuclei of atoms of all kinds, stripped of all their outer electrons. They come in towards the earth from outer space in substantially the same proportions in which they exist everywhere in the material world—hydrogen nuclei, or protons, vastly in the ascendant; helium nuclei, the alpha-particles of the Geiger counter, second; and then a whole string of the nuclei of the heavier elements, in very much smaller quantity.

Whence they all come from is still unknown. A very few— less than a millionth of the total arriving at the earth—come from the sun: for very occasionally, as happened for example in

February 1956, a solar flare may throw out a group of particles moving so much faster than those normally responsible for magnetic storms that they are classified as slow cosmic rays. But the vast majority of the charged atomic nuclei of the cosmic rays must come from other stars or galaxies.

They arrive in the earth's upper atmosphere mainly at very high speed, gained most probably in the cosmic accelerating machines of the interstellar magnetised gas-clouds. Practically none of these primary particles from outer space reach the earth's surface: they are destroyed in explosive collisions with the oxygen and nitrogen nuclei in the atmosphere, giving birth to a bewildering variety of secondary particles, such as the much-discussed short-lived mesons.

In the last decade the study of cosmic rays has been predominantly the study of these strange short-lived particles, the mesons and the hyperons. But quite recently the attention of cosmic-ray physicists has been directed more particularly to their use as a probe in the investigation of the earth's magnetic field: and this is the reason for the inclusion of cosmic rays as one of the scientific disciplines in the IGY.

This change of focus in cosmic-ray physics has two consequences: in the first place, interest is concentrated, not on the fastest primaries, which yield the most exciting fleeting new particles, but on the slower particles from outer space, which are most affected by the earth's field; in the second place, the most important products of the nuclear explosions high aloft are no longer the fleeting mesons, but the long-lived neutrons which reach the earth to tell how far the primaries have penetrated the outer atmosphere.

The chief tool of the new approach is thus the *neutron counter*, a device which ticks off the number of neutrons arising from the nuclear explosions aloft. The neutron counter records in fact the number of primary particles which penetrate the outer regions of the earth's magnetic field.

Concentrating our attention, then, on the slow moving primary particles approaching the earth from outer space: they will be deflected north and south towards the earth's magnetic poles, the more strongly the slower they are moving;

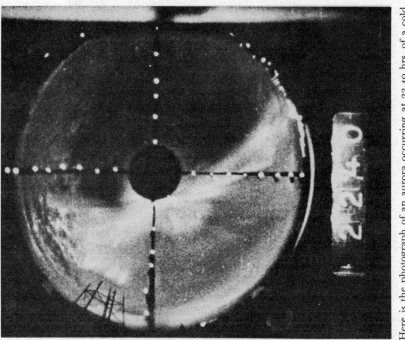

Here is the photograph of an aurora occurring at 22.40 hrs. of a cold arctic evening, as seen in the all-sky camera.

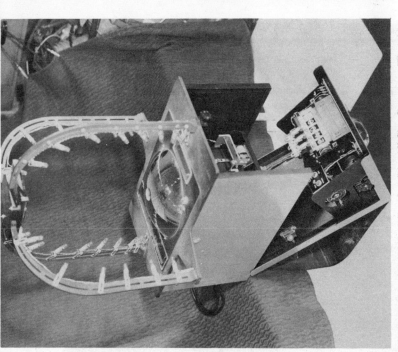

The most recent model of the Gartlein All-Sky Camera. The cine-camera, enclosed in the same housing as the 24-hour clock, takes its pictures through a hole in the centre of the convex lens, by reflection in a mirror supported by four girders, which carry small pilot lights determining the position of the aurora in both azimuth and altitude.

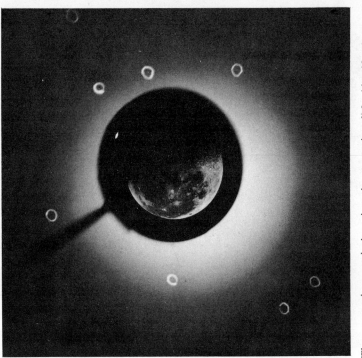

The moon photographed against the stars, ringed for identification and measurement. During the exposure, the image of the moon is held sharp and stationary by tilting the dark filter through a small angle, at just the right speed, by means of an accurate mechanical drive.

An over-all view of the Markowitz Moon Camera, as seen from the back, showing the dark filter which reduces the brightness of the moon's image by about 1000, thus allowing the exposure of 20 seconds which is needed for a clear picture of the surrounding stars.

so that we should expect a *minimum* in the count of the neutrons arriving in our counters at the earth's Geomagnetic Equator.

Already we know that this is not the case. Neutron counters were carried on the American survey ship *Atka* to and fro across the Equator in 1954–55; and the counts have revealed that the magnetic equator for the cosmic rays is slewed backwards against the direction of the earth's rotation, as if the

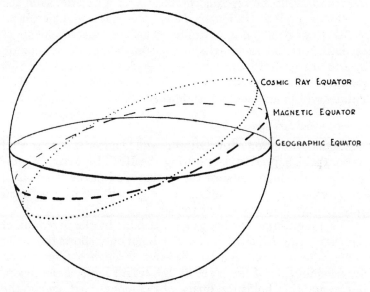

COSMIC RAY EQUATOR

MAGNETIC EQUATOR

GEOGRAPHIC EQUATOR

The magnetic equator for slow cosmic rays is not the same as that determined by observations made on a compass needle at the earth's surface.

magnetic field of the earth were distorted in its outer reaches by an electrically conducting medium.

This is a most exciting discovery. It can only mean that the earth and its atmospheric sheath is not moving in a perfect vacuum at all: that either the thin cosmic clouds of the Milky Way penetrate to the earth's immediate environment, or that perhaps the sun's tenuous corona extends so far from the sun's visible disc that the earth is enveloped in it.

Forty-odd neutron monitors installed for the IGY at places like Fort Churchill, Minneapolis, Buenos Aires, Sao Paulo:

Stockholm, Rome, Kampala, Hermanus: Murmansk, Dar-jeeling, Colombo, Auckland will surely have a tale to tell!

Seismology and gravity

Here are two disciplines which have been included in the IGY programme as a matter of convenience rather than of necessity. Neither has a genuine need even for a concentrated *epochal* study, to be repeated perhaps after a decade, as in the case for example of glaciology. Nevertheless, it would have been foolish to neglect the opportunity of making measurements of earthquakes and of gravity in regions where no systematic measurements have hitherto been made—in Antarctica, for example, or on remote islands in the oceans, where IGY stations will in any case be established.

Latitudes and longitudes

A redetermination of the latitudes and longitudes of 20 special stations will be undertaken during the IGY, by taking photographs of the moon against the background of the fixed stars, on every clear night during the eighteen months between July 1, 1957, and the end of 1958.

This programme has been made possible by the invention of the Markowitz Moon Camera, which not only allows the moon to be photographed against the stars through a filter which prevents fogging of the plate by the bright light of the moon, but in addition holds the image of the moon fixed against the star background during the exposure.

Now the position of the moon in its orbit at any one instant, as entered in the astronomical tables of the moon's motion, is the position in which it would be seen at that instant by an imaginary observer located at the centre of the earth. The real observer sees it displaced from its astronomical position by an amount which depends on his position on the earth's surface, and by his distance from the earth's centre. Hence by repeated observations of the moon's position made at any one point on the earth's surface, not only its latitude and longitude, but also the corresponding value for the radius of the earth can be calculated. By combining the values of the earth's radius as measured at 20 different stations, there should result a far more accurate idea of the true size and shape of the earth than any we have at present.

The estimated precision with which the position of a point on the earth's surface can be determined by means of the Markowitz moon camera is indeed so high that a most exciting possibility presents itself: namely, that a series of observations, spread over a sufficient lapse of time, might tell us whether the land masses of the world are still drifting over its surface or not. Thus the moon-position programme of the IGY not only leads immediately to more accurate maps of the world; it is also an epochal programme, which by repetition in the future might give evidence of a contemporary continental drift.

Further, accurate observations of the moon's changing position throughout the year can give a new check on the seasonal changes in the earth's speed of rotation. This is done by a comparison of the calculated position of the moon among the fixed stars at any one time, on the assumption that the earth is rotating uniformly, with the position as actually observed. This comparison can be made with an altogether new degree of accuracy with the aid of the Markowitz moon camera. Also for the first time, the meteorologists will have full information during the IGY about the variation in the seasonal winds north and south of the Equator; and a re-calculation of the cause of the seasonal variations in the length of the day will be by no means impossible.

CHAPTER 9

ROCKETS AND SATELLITES

BEFORE the end of the year 1957, the earth will in all for-
seeable probability have acquired another moon. . . .

For both the United States and Soviet Russia have far-
reaching plans to place artificial earth satellites in the sky during the period of the International Geophysical Year. They are
doing so not as a stunt, nor as a competitive item in a "space
race", but as an integrated part of the overall programme of
the IGY.

Here are the cold words of the recommendation made at the
historic meeting in Rome in 1954:

> "In view of the great importance of observations during
> extended periods of time of extraterrestrial radiations and
> geophysical phenomena in the upper atmosphere, and in view
> of the advanced state of present rocket techniques, the Special
> Committee for the International Geophysical Year recom-
> mends that thought be given to the launching of small satel-
> lite vehicles."

With these official words as text, let us look at their inner
meaning.

Observations of the ionosphere made from the earth's surface,
valuable as they are, are conditioned by the fact that just those
agents that act to produce its most characteristic properties—
solar ultra-violet radiation, solar X-rays, meteors, cosmic rays,
corpuscles from the sun during magnetic storms—never penetrate to ground-level. Thus the whole mechanism behind the
production and man-made use of the ionosphere, or the complex phenomena of the aurora, or the existence of the night
airglow, has to be deduced with the help of theoretical pictures
of what *could* be happening far aloft. Many of the deductions,
as we have seen, are so closely self-consistent that there is no

reasonable doubt that they are essentially correct. But *direct* observation of the conditions 50 or 100 or even 200 miles and more above the earth's surface is the real criterion.

Such direct observation has indeed become possible during the last decade through the medium of high-altitude rocket flights. This method has, however, two grave disadvantages: first, it is extremely costly—at least £10,000 for one actual rocket, apart altogether from the cost of the necessary installations—and second, there are only 2 or 3 minutes, during the flight of the rocket, in which to gather the data we are looking for. The second disadvantage, although decidedly not the first, is eliminated by the use of an artificial satellite, which stays up there for weeks or months on end, telemetering its information back to earth on demand.

An artificial satellite needs a rocket, however, and a three-stage rocket at that, to launch it in its orbit 200 or 300 miles above the earth. So the story of earth satellites must begin with the story of the development of rocket techniques.

Swords and ploughshares

Modern rocketry began with the German V2 during World War II. The V2 was the brain-child of Werner von Braun, a man who was then, and now as a United States citizen still is, primarily interested in rockets as vehicles for space flight. In 1945 the United States acquired upwards of a hundred V2's, together with their inventor, and the direct scientific exploration of the upper atmosphere was launched with the first V2 to ascend from White Sands, New Mexico, on April 16, 1946, carrying instruments for the observation of man's environment, instead of high explosives, in its nose.

You could say that here the sword had been beaten into a ploughshare. But that isn't really the point. The fact of the matter is that almost every scientific discovery is a two-edged sword, and you can't blame it on God if man insists on honing the wrong edge. As far as rockets (or indeed satellites) are concerned, the choice is still open to mankind: whether to continue to use them for scientific exploration, or to go hunting the Snark with them instead. But for 1957-58, at any rate, there is a rocket programme with not one single Boojum in it.

The IGY Rocket Programme

The United States alone will fire over 200 rockets during the IGY, from launching grounds as far north as Fort Churchill in Canada to Little America, far south in the Antarctic. The U.S.S.R. has its own extensive programme, details of which, however, were not available at the last meeting of the IGY Special Committee held at Barcelona in September 1956. Japan will fire ten or twelve rockets between July 1957 and the close of 1958. Britain will fire some twenty rockets from the Woomera Rocket Range in Australia.

The time-table of rocket firings during the IGY takes full account of the Regular World Days, on which particularly concentrated observations in all the different scientific disciplines will be made. In this way, direct comparisons can be made between the probings of the upper atmosphere from the ground and the direct if fleeting observations of the same phenomena telemetered back to earth from rockets soaring 100 miles and more above the earth's surface. Attempts will also be made to launch rockets during World Alerts, although here there are severe technical difficulties, particularly in the case of the larger rockets, such as the American Aerobee, which demand at least 12 hours and possibly a full day's preparation for firing, even assuming that all the instruments are already installed. The possibilities are greater for the smaller balloon-launched rockets, or Rockoons, for once the balloon carrying the rocket is aloft, the rocket itself can be fired in a matter of seconds by radio from the ground. The technique of launching small rockets from high-flying aircraft is also being studied, particularly in the United States.

Vertical cross-section

The observations in the upper atmosphere which will be made from the rockets launched during the IGY yield a vertical cross-section through a majority of the separate scientific disciplines which we have surveyed in horizontal plan in the preceding chapter. Data of crucial importance to meteorology, ionospheric physics, the study of the aurora, geomagnetism, cosmic rays, will be gathered by the instruments sent aloft in the nose-caps of Aerobees, Nike-Cajuns, Rockoons, the Japanese Kappa, and the British Skylark. . . . Let us have a look at some of the more interesting of the devices which will be used.

Solar Radiation

Measurements of solar radiation, unfiltered by the atmosphere, are of fundamental importance. Spectroscopic records in the far ultra-violet are already an established part of rocket technique. Stabilised platforms on which to mount the spectroscopes, which automatically oblige them to face the sun in spite of the rolling and pitching of the rocket vehicle, have already been developed, thus allowing the maximum length of exposure of the photographic film on which the imprint of the ultra-violet spectrum is taken. The technique of recovery of the photographic records from the wreckage of the fallen rocket has also already been worked out, such recovery necessitating of course the launching of the rocket from a site in uninhabited country. During the IGY, rocket spectrograms will be taken farther out into the ultra-violet than ever before. The farthest ultra-violet and the X-ray spectrum of the sun will also be studied by means of special counting devices, particularly during the appearance of solar flares: in this case the information is telemetered from the rocket back to earth during the period of flight.

High-level winds : Grenades and Sodium Bombs

At least two methods, one already well established, the other quite novel, will be employed to study the winds which radio-science has already shown to occur in the upper reaches of the atmosphere, high above both troposphere and stratosphere.

The first method, hitherto usable only by night, is known as the *grenade method*. Here the rocket vehicle carries a number of grenades, which it shoots out sideways at predetermined intervals, once it has attained the required height. Each grenade carries a time-fuse, so that it explodes well away—

some 200 feet to be exact—from the rocket. The flash of the explosion is recorded by a ring of photocells girdling the parent rocket, and is immediately telemetered back to earth. The in-

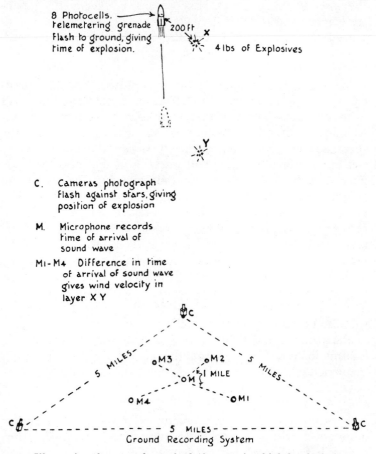

Illustrating the grenade method of measuring high level winds.

stant of explosion is therefore known. Three cameras on the ground, placed in a triangle 5 miles apart, photograph the same flash against the stars, so that the position of the grenade at the instant of explosion is determined. A microphone on the ground records the time of arrival of the sound of the explosion.

Launching an Aerobee rocket at White Sands, New Mexico.

This is what the earth looks like to an Aerobee soaring above it at a height of 100 miles.

From these data the velocity of sound in the layer of the upper atmosphere lying between two successive exploding grenades can at once be determined—and thereby the *temperature* of the layer in question, since the velocity of sound in air depends thereon.

Now the master microphone on the ground is surrounded by four others, placed about 1 mile away. If there is no horizontal wind in the layer aloft, which is marked off by the explosions of two successive grenades, then all four microphones will record the sounds of their explosions simultaneously: otherwise, the microphone farthest downwind will receive the signals first. It is in this ingenious way that the winds far in the upper air can be charted.

Observation of the winds in the ionosphere is one of the chief items in the British rocket programme of the IGY, to be carried out at Woomera in Australia, the first launching of which took place successfully on St. Valentine's Day 1957. An interesting refinement, among several others, is the operation of the camera shutters on the ground by the flash-signal from the rocket, thus allowing the method to be operated in the daytime without fogging the photographic film. . . .

The second method, for which pioneer experiments have already been carried out, proposes to eject a canister of metallic sodium, to be vaporised by a charge of thermite, from a rocket cruising 50 miles or so above earth. The luminous vapour, shining with the well-known yellow light of sodium, can then be traced as it disperses, driven before the high-level winds!

Dynamo Currents

We have seen in Chapter 4 how the daily variation of the compass needle can be accounted for by postulating the existence of powerful currents in the sunlit ionosphere, which arise from the tidal action of the sun on the earth's atmosphere. During the IGY, rockets will effectively carry compass needles aloft, into the regions where the dynamo currents are supposed to flow, in the shape of sensitive recording magnetometers. In this way, direct measurement of these so far hypothetical currents should be possible.

Particle Studies

An intensive drive will be made by the American rocket group to identify the particles from the sun which are reckoned to give rise to the aurora, and to learn more about their direction of arrival in the auroral zones, and their connection with eruptions on the sun.

To this end they have collaborated with the Canadians to equip an entirely new rocket-firing base at Fort Churchill near Hudson Bay. The Canadians have provided the site and the local facilities; the Americans are footing the bill of some millions of dollars. The site, lying well within the Arctic auroral zone, is an ideal one; and out of a total of seventy-five rocket firings planned for Fort Churchill during the IGY, no less than twenty are earmarked for the direct observation of auroral particles.

Other particles which will receive special attention in the rocket programme are the low-energy primary cosmic rays, some of which may occasionally originate in the sun. We have already learned of the interesting information about the earth's magnetic field which the most recent studies of the low-energy cosmic rays has yielded. But these studies were made at the earth's surface, by observation of secondary effects; so confirmation of the new findings by the direct observation from rockets of the low-energy primaries themselves is eagerly awaited.

Long-playing rocket

The flight of a rocket is over in a matter of a few hectic minutes. Hence the advantage, apart from any other considerations (which are considerable), of an artificial earth satellite which can be expected to orbit the globe for several weeks, or even months. The American inventors have in fact labelled their satellite the "long-playing rocket".

The launching of an artificial satellite in a stable orbit stretches to the utmost the resources of the most advanced modern rocket techniques. There are two separate considerations which emphasise the boldness of the whole conception. First, the satellite must be launched horizontally, with a precision of less than a degree, for otherwise its orbit would be so eccentric an ellipse as to be of negligible practical use. Secondly, the height at which the satellite is launched must be high enough above ground-level to give it a reasonable useful life. To appreciate the force of this argument, it is only necessary to state that a satellite successfully launched at a height of 200 miles has an

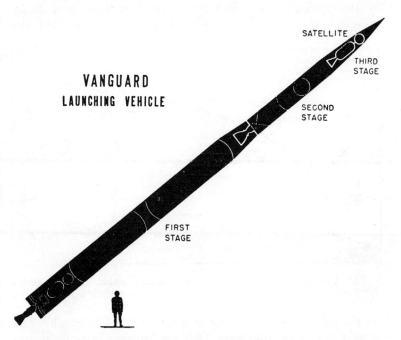

VANGUARD
LAUNCHING VEHICLE

SATELLITE

THIRD
STAGE

SECOND
STAGE

FIRST
STAGE

A rocket vehicle weighing 11 tons is needed to launch an earth satellite weighing just over 20 lbs.

expectation of life against the drag of the residual atmosphere at that level of only a fortnight, whereas one launched at a height of 300 miles can look to a span of several months or even a year. In either event the friction of the tenuous atmospheric pressure aloft eventually brakes the speed of the flying bird until it drops spiralling earthwards, burning itself to a cinder like any other meteor in its descent.

Three-stage launch

The American satellites will be launched from a gigantic three-stage rocket, known as the *Vanguard*. The Vanguard is a finless rocket, 72 feet long, 45 inches round its middle, weight 11 tons. It is designed to be launched vertically, to be immediately guided from the ground to move at an angle of 45° to the vertical. The first stage, burning a mixture of liquid oxygen and alcohol, drops away 36 miles from base, with the

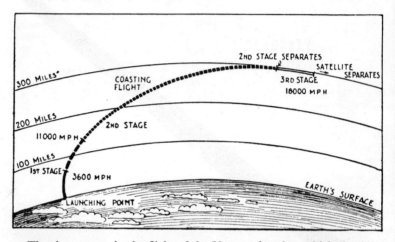

The three stages in the flight of the Vanguard rocket, which should launch the first artificial satellite before the close of the year 1957.

combination vehicle moving at a speed of 3,600 m.p.h. The second stage, an improved Aerobee, burning nitric acid and hydrazine, then takes over, to carry the vehicle 140 miles from base, reaching a speed of 11,000 m.p.h. at burn-out. The vehicle then coasts onwards until, flying horizontally, it is 300 miles from base, the speed having dropped to 9,000 m.p.h. The second stage now separates, 10 minutes after take-off, and the third stage, charged with a solid propellant, boosts the speed to 18,000 m.p.h., 1,500 miles from the launching point. Finally, the satellite itself, carried in the nose of the third stage, separates: spherical in shape, 20 inches in diameter, weight just over 20 lb.!

Chosen orbit

The United States Satellite Group are preparing a round dozen of these tiny objects, each one packed with miniaturised instruments for the observation of conditions 300 miles above the earth. Contrary to prevalent ideas, even the first "bird" to be sent aloft will carry instruments, for the chances of placing any of the twelve successfully in a stable orbit are great enough to justify banking on initial success and subsequent failure.

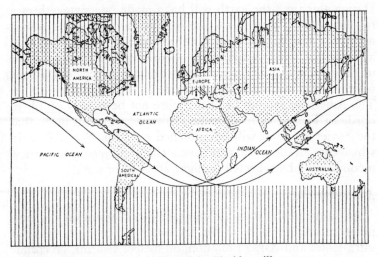

The American satellites, launched in Florida, will sweep out a zone lying between 40° north and south of the equator.

The base from which the giant Vanguard rockets will be launched is the Patrick Air Force Base at Cape Canaveral, on the east coast of Florida. The rockets will be guided during the operation of the first stage south-eastwards, at an angle of around 40° to the Equator. This choice of direction is conditioned by a variety of reasons: among them the need to have the first two stages drop off over water where shipping has been suspended, and the advantage of gaining the sling-shot effect of the rotating earth in launching the satellite in its orbit.

Although aimed at a circular orbit at an altitude of 300 miles, the satellites will probably take up an elliptical orbit, with closest approach to the earth of about 200 miles and most distant retreat of perhaps 1,000 miles. At the speed of 18,000 miles an hour, the force of gravity is exactly balanced by the centrifugal force of the moving satellite, so that the orbit is stable, apart from the inevitable braking effect of the tenuous atmosphere which is still present at an altitude of 300 miles.

The satellite will traverse its orbit once every hour and a half. During this time the earth will have made one sixteenth of a revolution from west to east, so that at each successive transit across the equator the track of the satellite will on this account alone be displaced westwards by about 22·5° of longitude. Thus in the course of many transits the satellite sweeps out a zone which girdles the earth from latitude 40° N. to latitude 40° S. The American satellites will therefore not be readily visible in northern Europe or in Canada. However, it seems likely that the Soviet satellites will be launched over the North Pole, in which case all the world can have a chance of seeing a tiny new moon shining by reflected sunlight at dawn or dusk.

Moon's-eye view

An instrumented satellite can take observations on the temperature and pressure of the far outer atmosphere, on solar ultra-violet and X-ray radiation, on meteor swarms, on cosmic rays, and perhaps even track the corpuscles from the sun which give rise to magnetic storms and auroral displays on earth. In fact, as we have said, it can do everything that rockets have already done, but for several weeks instead of for a few minutes. There are, however, in the meantime at least, two disadvantages which the satellite has against the rocket: first, its small size and weight, which set cruel limits on the type of instrument it can carry; and second, the fact that it is not recoverable, since it is moving at such a high speed as it eventually spirals back to earth that it is reduced to ashes by the friction of the surrounding air. This latter disadvantage rules out the use of photographic methods, including the possibility of taking visual pictures of the cloud-cover of the earth.

The chain of radio tracking stations designed to ensure the acquisition
of the earth's first artificial satellites.

Acquisition

Apart altogether from such instrumental observations aloft, which an artificial satellite makes possible, the accurate tracking of the satellite from the ground offers a unique opportunity for a closer study of the shape of the earth; and the American plans lay heavy emphasis on this item of the satellite programme.

But before the satellite can be tracked in its orbit, it must first be "acquired": that is, it must be spotted and held under observation from below as soon as possible after the moment of its separation from the third stage of its rocket vehicle. This phase of the experiment is going to be a nerve-racking ordeal for all concerned.

First reliance must be placed on spotting the bird by radio, which is of course independent of cloudy weather conditions. The satellites will carry a radio-transmitter, operating on a frequency of 108 megacycles (and incidentally, this is the agreed frequency for *all* satellites, Russian or American, so that each can track the other's). A chain of eight receiving stations, strung out along the 75° W. meridian from Washington in the north to Santiago Brazil in the south, have been building apace during the year 1956, in readiness for their job of spotting the first satellite as it sweeps past overhead. This is an even trickier proceeding than might appear at first sight: for the cramped space inside the 20-inch-diameter sphere cannot allow the installation of batteries capable of operating the transmitter continuously—it must be triggered by a signal from below just before the satellite is reckoned to be approaching the 75° W. meridian.

Once acquired, the most accurate method of tracking the satellite is by means of specially designed cameras of large aperture, strategically placed at such locations as White Sands, New Mexico; the Netherlands Antilles; Antofagasta, Chile; Bloemfontein, South Africa; Kodaikanal, India; Southern Japan.

The figure of the earth

If the earth were completely uniform and spherical, the orbit of the satellite would, as we have seen, be displaced west-

Construction work in progress at the new rocket base at Fort Churchill, near Hudson Bay in Canada, specifically designed for observations within the arctic auroral zone during the IGY.

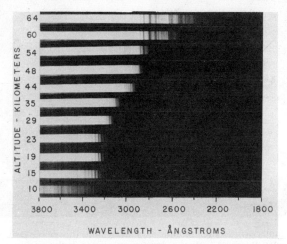

Records of the sun's spectrum taken from an ascending Aerobee rocket. The greater the height, the more of the sun's ultra-violet radiation is received in the air-borne spectrographs.

The satellite itself, mirror-polished to reduce residual atmospheric friction to a minimum. The projecting aerials radio news of conditions 300 miles above earth to the receiving stations below.

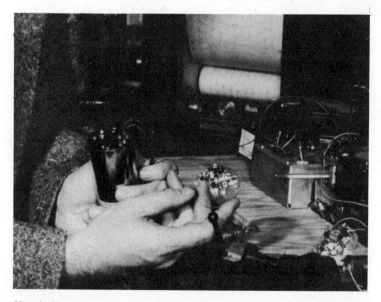

Here is the miniaturised radio transmitter, along with its tiny power-pack, which will send coded messages from the instruments carried in the satellite back to earth.

ward by 22·5° between successive transits of the Equator, by the mere fact that the earth is turning eastward beneath it. But the earth bulges at the Equator; and so every time the satellite crosses it, only 300 miles up, the extra gravitational pull of the bulge will speed it up slightly. This temporary increase in speed has the effect of putting a westward twist on the orbit in which the satellite is moving, so that instead

The bulge of the earth at the Equator causes the plane of the satellite's orbit to edge westwards. The orbit illustrated here is rather different from that chosen for the U.S. satellite, so as to show the effect more clearly.

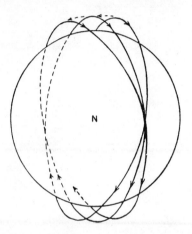

of the successive transits being 22·5° apart, there will be more like 25° between them. The *accurate* determination of this difference in longitude—and the potential accuracy is very high—would give us a new look at the exact figure of the earth, in addition to that which we expect to get from the first use of the moon camera.

More: the optical tracking of the satellite, if successful, is so sensitive that minor perturbations of the orbit, arising from a lack of uniformity of the earth's crust, should be measurable. A sort of celestial geology may, in fact, be just around the corner.

Death spiral

The useful life of an artificial satellite is limited by the density of the atmosphere in which it is launched. Even at 300 miles aloft there is still enough air to brake its speed until gravity wins over centrifugal force, and the satellite spirals earthwards until the ever-denser air heats it to incandescence, so that it breaks up into glowing fragments, which are then largely vaporised. Accurate observations of the change of speed with time, and particularly of the ultimate death spiral, should allow a real determination of the variation of the density of the upper atmosphere with height, to replace the crude guesses which are all we have been able to hazard so far.

CHAPTER 10

THE SUMMING UP

A PERFECTLY legitimate question may now be posed: namely, what is to be gained from the gigantic enterprise of the International Geophysical Year, uniting as it does the thought and effort of the scientists of fifty-four countries, costing as it must millions of pounds, involving inevitably the setting up of over a thousand observational stations, in the Arctic, in the Antarctic, or athwart the Equator?

The modern gnostics might answer that the very fact that so many different countries are banded together in a common task is in itself a sufficient justification for the whole undertaking. And indeed, they would be not so far off the mark: for to anyone who has seen the whole development of the enterprise from its modest beginnings back in 1950, one of its most shining facets has been the practical demonstration of the truth that, given a certain attainable threshold of mutual interest, men of all nations are willing, nay eager, to join in a drive towards the same goal. Not merely to discuss the matter, but to do something about it.

Now scientists may be enthusiasts, sometimes they may allow themselves to be used as tools: but their training makes them innately sceptical of words which have taken on a life of their own. They genuinely want to see results—and they confidently expect to see very tangible results coming out of the IGY effort in 1957–58.

On the practical side, which immediately affects the lives of the majority of mankind, they expect to see at least three consequences of the intensive attack on the secrets of man's environment during the eighteen months of the IGY.

First, there is the strong possibility that, as the outcome of the multitudinous observations on the global circulation of the lower atmosphere, the meteorologists may arrive at such an increased measure of their understanding of the turbulent air that long-range weather prediction, happily assisted by the contemporaneous development of electronic calculating machines, may at last become an accomplished fact. The practical results to agriculture, to shipping, to air navigation need not be stressed.

Second come the probings of the upper atmosphere, the ionosphere of radio communication, made simultaneously in the strategic regions within the Arctic and Antarctic Circles, and in the Equatorial Zone, by a dozen different methods. The men who are engaged on these aspects of the whole programme look to a new era of smooth and certain radio transmission, even during periods of magnetic storms.

Thirdly, the cartographers already see maps of the world in their minds' eye of another degree of accuracy, resulting from the use of the moon camera, and from the successful tracking of the artificial satellites.

The word "practical", however, has a very relative meaning. Today's academic discovery may well be tomorrow's bread and circus. Tomorrow's merely elegant scientific result may be next week's industrial winner. So such seemingly impractical answers to present scientific queries as may come out of the IGY effort: as for instance the question whether the aurora borealis and the aurora australis occur always simultaneously, or not; or whether the magnetic equator for the cosmic rays is really different from that of the earth-bound magnetic compass; or where the sodium in the sodium layer comes from; or whether the small magnetic storms originate in the coronal streamers or in spicules on the sun's disc; or why sunspots change their magnetic polarity at each sunspot cycle—such answers may sooner or later have far-reaching consequences to the life of mankind on earth. . . .

Even then we haven't got to the heart of the matter: that such answers are answers in their own right, whether they ever have any practical bearing or not. As Fridtjof Nansen so cogently put it: "Man wants to know, and when he ceases to do so he is no longer man."